COLOR

AWAKENING THE CHILD WITHIN

JULIANNE BIEN

spectrahue
light & sound inc.
TORONTO

Published and distributed by
Spectrahue Light & Sound Inc.
P.O. Box 85507
842 Eglinton Avenue West
Toronto, Ontario
Canada M5N 0A2

(416) 340.0882
www.spectrahue.com

Library and Archives Canada Cataloguing in Publication

Bien, Julianne
        Color : awakening the child within / Julianne Bien.

ISBN 0-9734835-1-2

        I. Title.

PS8603.I35C65 2006   C813'.6   C2006-903423-0

Second Printing.

First Edition.
Printed on chlorine-free recycled paper.
Printed and bound in Canada.

Dedicated to
the Voice in all of us.

Cosmic conception.

The time-space continuum.

Its genesis exists in the mind of a poet.

It does not exist outside oneself.

Discover its essence with an inward spin.

The odyssey through the universal mind provides

a view of creation behind the mirror of imagination,

before color transformed life.

PREFACE

Color: Awakening the Child Within, is a space odyssey fantasy for those who are forever young at heart. In our story, passed down through generations of the subconscious mind, seven galactic Pioneers journey through time and space in order to color/animate Earth and humanity. These characters are actually color photons who personify each color's magical qualities. Explore the creation of the human form from their point of view: inside-out!

The Prologue sets the stage of pre-creation. Science and folklore conceived of only one Big Bang in their theories of creation, but it was more like a series of cosmic breaths in the expansion of outer space. Our Storyteller, GrandPa GammaRay, shares the legend of the photonic Pioneers with the Children of the Multiverse. These Children represent the chemical aspects of reality in our universe. Discover who and what you are as you identify with the characters' unique quirks, quarks and idiosyncrasies.

This story is more than just a fantasy. It's an educational tool designed to teach you the essence of the language of light and its influence on the creation of our world.

Life is comprised of color energy. Every color of the light spectrum emits a unique intensity of energy based upon its wavelength. Colors are also electrically and magnetically charged. Biologically, life forms use electric and magnetic color as energy signals to organize and communicate at the cellular level and to transmit information throughout their bodies.

Colors exist in each of us, and in everything around us that we experience. Each color influences us emotionally, physically, psychologically and spiritually. Although we may think that color effects are quite subtle in nature, our memories and experiences are actually stored as energy imprints in the human bioenergy field (aura) surrounding our bodies.

Color and light are now being explored and applied worldwide in the healthcare industry. It is to this end that I wish to inform the reader about the true nature of color light for its communicative ability for personal growth and awareness.

Creating this book was a wonderful adventure. My heartfelt appreciation goes to all those who helped me along the way.

Julianne Bien
Toronto, 2006

PROLOGUE

Once within a time—space continuum, eons before perception.

Time stood still.
It was and was not.
It began and began not.
There was Space.
A vastness of nothingness.
A blend of everythingness.
Without beginning and ending.

Order and Chaos.
Involution of darkness.
Evolution of light.
The Cosmos emerged.
A harmonic symphony.
Sonic surges of vibrations.
Verses cascaded in rhythms.
Stellar structures rose in awareness.
They swayed, swirled and bowed.

Elements, gases and dust particles gathered.
Creation of atomic matter spun into form.
Form shaped infinite celestial bodies.

Stardust unified bodies into galaxies and fashioned realms.
Celestial beings expanded and ricocheted outward.
Nebulous plasma spread across the Void.

Eternal light created an orderly system of coherence.
Interstellar communication emerged.
Celestial bodies sounded off vibrations throughout the Cosmos.
Echoed responses fired back into the silence.
The expanding canvass of Space spread darkness.
Nothing and Everything stretched across the ethers.

The holographic sphere of light evolved.
Eternal light emanated perception from its wholeness.
Perception encompassed thought and burst into sparks.
Subatomic spin with an outward force
Illuminated, spiraled and funneled into helixes.
Coiled then whirled within interconnected possibilities.

Infinite choice unveiled.
Dream within a dream.
Forces molded interdimensional space
Projected from the cosmic radiant fire of eternity.
The mirror of illusion resided in imagination.
Light revealed its shadowed reflection.

Order swerved and bowed as Chaos emerged.
Cosmic pressure crashed into waves of force.
Momentum built and collapsed obstacles,
Obliterated stellar structures and disintegrated planetary systems.
The expansion of creation extended across eternal blackness.
Cosmic, solar and lunar light flared across Space.
Mathematical ratios of stars lit worldly realms.

Silence shattered from The Bang.
Boom — the Cosmic breath bends and twists.
It created depth, breadth, width and height.
Genesis emerged out of abyss,
Galactically appeared out of the Void.
Boom — another Cosmic breath.

Intense pressure.
A sudden jolt.
The colossal cosmic clock halted as its dial sloped in honor.
Space stood still in awe.
Out of the darkness galactic waters surged and
Funneled downward into the Universal Mind.

The Cosmic scale appeared,
The balance of weights and measures.
Energy forces separated into oppositions.
The helix chain carved from its tension.
Layers of numbers and letters appeared
Inscribed in the ethers.

Phi emerged from nothingness.
It plotted eternity as it playfully twisted in delight.
Cosmic geometrical particles intertwined forming realities.
Formulas and keys are coded as star coordinates,
The Universal links to the Infinite Mind.

Time continuums merged within intergalactic space.
Thought formed and activated consciousness.
Energy in opposition weaved and twisted in reflection.
The waltz of equality.
A dance of polarity.

Light spoke,
Illuminated sound and action.
An eternal archetypical tree appeared.
Wisdom and knowledge carved within its depth.
Branches reached across eternity.
Roots spiraled deep into the Earth.

Positive magnetic force of the golden Sun
Challenged the electric coolness of the Moon.
Tottered rhythms in its cycles.
Fueled and directed throughout the helical weave.
Each cycle influenced celestial wholeness.
A keynote sounded.
A celestial song emerged.

Two hundred thirty-one gates appeared.
Thirty-two paths of wisdom.
Thirty-two states of consciousness.
Twenty-two doors of knowledge.
Ten directions of nothingness.

Crystalline spherical vessels aligned.
A twelve-segmented celestial sphere blossomed,
Each assigned an archetype
To influence cosmic projections.
Ponder and probe within the Inquisitive Mind.

The Metaverse birthed a Multiverse.
The Universe separated and descended.
A three-dimensional playground for Humankind.
Polarity by tension coaxed energy into motion,
Casted infinite reflections across vast lightness.
Mirrored projections transcended and returned.

The cycle of breath: illuminated.
Earth's creation rose from perception.
Solarized. Colorized. Personified. Animated.
Imagination blossomed infinite possibilities.
The colossal holographic sphere of All.

Tread its cosmic waters if you dare.
Delve into the deepest caverns of your psyche.
Climb the forty-nine steps of the helix staircase.
Pass through each door and explore its centers.
Search within the energy of each color to unlock its code,
Revealing universal secrets of the Earthly realms.

Join the odyssey of the cosmic masquerade.

The story began with a Boom.
Some say a cosmic breath.
It unraveled from this point,
and never stopped.
Meet our storyteller, GrandPa GammaRay,
the Children of the Multiverse
and the Voice.
The color violet begins the story
as the cosmic clock sounded 11:11

CHAPTER ONE

Faster than cosmic flares of lightning
The Universe expanding, contracting and tightening
The cosmic breath electrifying, cooling and clever
Cracking the secret code of creation hidden in Mind forever

— Violet

Crackle Zippen-Poof. The Earth trembled. The Voice rattled the spherical rim of the Earth's ionosphere with his vibration spewing violet and gold streams of energy and swirls of gaseous forms everywhere. Powerful currents elevated as curdling undertones rode the waves of his overtones. The vibration ripped across the skies leaving streaks of effervescent silvery bubbles in his path. The Voice parted the luminous Heavens with thunderous notes and cataclysmic chimes. Whoosh! Yet another galactic tantrum. The Voice had a legendary mandate to be known. Chickles, chuckles and cackling sounds burst in from outer galaxies smoothing out the heavenly screen with equanimity. Their peaceful resonance playfully coaxed the Voice to recoil and snap back out of chaos and into a state of order. He perched on an octave bar suspended by the tension of gaseous flares of fire. The Voice is the cosmic force of universal creation.

THE VOICE DREW BACK HIS BREATH

With an inward heave, the Voice drew back his breath and gathered the dispersed cosmic pressure and stardust. Instantly, he orchestrated a symbiotic symphony of dancing swirls of color as the Angelic Realms looked on in amazement. The Angels took great pleasure in striking these chords of color that sounded in resonance. The music of the spheres created rhythm for the universal cycles of life.

The Voice stilled his force into silence. The clouds gazed upward and drifted dreamily back into position. They were suddenly parted by the Voice as he entered Earth's atmosphere. Enchanted with potential possibilities, the Voice whistled beams of light through the carved gateways of the Heavens, creating a cryptic passage in the atmosphere. In a sonic boom he engraved an indelible imprint in the consciousness of the ionosphere surrounding Earth:

Human consciousness is an evolutionary cyclical escapade laced with opportunity and the choice of free will. The beauty of life lies in its unlimited opportunities. This story sets the stage for the personification of life on Earth. It begins when Earth was an infant and nearly collapsed her celestial structure as she gasped and sputtered while taking her first cosmic breath. Her heart began to putter, sway and swill to the rhythm of the cosmic dance inviting the possibility to rerecord its destiny.

The Heavens shuddered in excitement as the Voice heaved in his cosmic force and slipped back through a passageway in the sky. The clouds weaved back into a universal mask to disguise the Heavens.

At this pivotal moment when the skies were opened, a group of children from the 49th Dimension's *Order of the Aspects of Reality* had taken this opportunity to glide through before the clouds interlocked. The cracking open of the gateway had been calculated to precise coordinates when they were conceived. Doors of opportunity swung open and slammed shut sequentially. To explore worldly realms in an orderly manner exact time slots were paramount.

The Children successfully passed through the watery gateway and squealed with a sense of accomplishment by singing the following song,

> *Here's a clue to discover your eternal cosmic treasure,*
> *Phi is the mathematical formula of life's eternal measure,*
> *Aspects of Reality are the Children of the Multiverse,*
> *one and the same,*
> *Galactic Phi-ionospheres are spiritual Pioneers of*
> *the seven-tier internal flame.*
> *Children of the Multiverse are the Aspects of Reality,*
> *one and the same,*
> *Pioneers are color with Phi and the ionosphere*
> *in a seven-energy center reign.*

The Children are chemical aspects of the Voice's subconscious mind, also referred to as Subbie in most galaxies. They had assembled from the far reaches of the intergalactic realms for this occasion. They knew this juncture would provide a mystical encounter for all of them. Their passage in space was a long distance when measured in phi-light years. Kavillions of eons had collapsed and risen, and Subbie wanted her Children to know their true identity as it had been temporarily concealed from their eternal memory. They just needed to be reminded. GrandPa GammaRay agreed to be her voice as the storyteller. The star coordinates were in alignment for the cosmic truth to be unveiled and for Humankind to be illuminated.

Although each was unique in their light-spanning differences and chemical compositions, the Children instinctually felt familiar ties with one another as they were all related. Although they were highly intelligent celestial alchemists: the cosmic tricksters who knew the formulas of universal knowledge; their personalities were innocently playful and childlike.

The stargate that they had entered had now vanished. The Children flocked together and swooped down towards a shimmering platform that appeared in the atmosphere right before their inner senses. They gently surfaced atop an ethereal fluffy-puffy golden spherical disk of stardust. It created a gentle breeze as it hazily spun clockwise in the sky.

Poof Collosal-Umph. A stellar ruby structure appeared and rose upward as if to touch the Heavens. It embraced luminous particles of light to mold its form. Majestically, it blossomed into a ruby cushion-like throne that hovered over the disk. The ancient-of-ancients appeared as vapor then materialized into a brilliant shimmering globule. It then shapeshifted and transformed into a vast infinite being.

GRANDPA GAMMARAY ARRIVED ON TIME

GrandPa GammaRay arrived on time. He communicated to the Children through his glistening starry smile. His presence radiated around the perimeter of Earth. He instantly created a pulsating heartbeat for the planet. This was a moment to remember, as Earth, the celestial baby, gasped her first breath.

The Children floated softly above the disk as they focused their perceptions. They perked up in awe of GrandPa's presence as he magnified and amplified brilliance throughout the intergalactic realms. They listened closely to his first words.

"It all began with one breath in space. The cosmos loved the reaction and has never stopped breathing since. Its expansion project is endless. Tune your imagination into the cosmos and let us review the Voice's master expansion plan," exclaimed GrandPa, illuminated with exhilaration. He was brimming over with anticipation and then he lowered his voice to an undertone for the Childrens' subtle subsenses to grasp.

As he continued, "And now Humankind is swimming within its currents to the beat of the cosmic breath. You are the active aspects that helically spiral within human cells, forming their time continuums. Your descendents are exact self-replicates and will create mindmaps for the expansion of consciousness. The seven galactic space travelers were colorfully designed to be part of the Voice's plan of Human Awakening, which was already occurring in 49 alternate timelines of multiple reality. All worldly realms are created at different rates of energy. Each of your personalities is unique to the aspect you personify and you reflect this image on Earth."

A sense of restlessness overcame the Children. They were tickled-pink and turquoise-thrilled and started to flutter about in an excited state as they were now with GrandPa. Eventually they flopped into an exhausted gelatinous state and shed light on their identities with a jingle and a jangle:

"Golly-gee, who wouldn't be?
If I am you, then you are me,
The DNA and RNA,
In the guise of color frequencies."

GrandPa gazed intently at the Children. They were very curious. He raised his stature and levitated the golden oracle that was concealed in his ruby cushion. It was laced with glistening galactic jewels and cosmic swirls of color energy particles. He pointed it towards the first child, Alte Atom. Alte Atom hurled flipside then downside in a gust of energy. He attempted to molecularly maneuver his form and morphed into a jellyfish-like blob. The rest of the Children giggled joyfully as he gathered his senses.

"Alte Atom," said GrandPa. "I can see you have something to share."

Alte Atom wriggled and morphed into a more comfy shape. He reflected his consciousness towards a specific timeline where he reviewed an exact reenactment of GrandPa's storyline vibration. A little surprised at this memory recall from the past, Alte Atom immediately popped back to the present.

ALTE ATOM WIGGLED AND MORPHED

Telepathically he transmitted his query, "Why was planet Earth created as a spherical body, and not as a flat plane that parallels the planets of the Kapvon Galaxy, in the 7th plane of existence, as they have a similar life form?" Alte Atom was always one quantum leap ahead of thought, which created realities of eons past. He was quick to get to the crux of the matter or wave, depending upon his viewing angle. Alte Atom had an affinity to bilocate, which is a continual desire for any Atom. When he was in one location for too long he became impatient. He tilted his ethereal figure for a response or affirming signal from the others.

GrandPa listened and registered Alte Atom's solar-charged mind waves. Serenely, he waited until all of the Children shared their mind patterns.

Preppy Petky Proton fast-forwarded into the future and returned. Silently he questioned GrandPa whether the inhabitants of Earth were able to access free will within their hologram of light as he could. He believed that linear time moved in the tides of experience, and since he was relentless to outshine Alte Atom and the others with his brightness and charisma, he needed to

PETKY PROTON FAST-FORWARDED

be one parallel universe ahead all the time. He felt that only a Proton could know the secret to free will and positive thinking and that he would show Humankind the way.

However, Petky Proton was supportive of Alte Atom and influenced the other Children of the Multiverse. Petky was magnetic and positively charged all the time, a completely opposite reflection than Elcy Electron. Petky was Alte Atom's building block and his stellar support system. They needed each other. GrandPa intuitively knew the Children were already phi-light years ahead in the story as they were given galactic authority to travel between realities.

"Did Humankind reclaim their birthright of magical powers?" echoed the eccentric Elcy Electron. "Rumor has it that the human body is comprised of a mineral-based substance and brought to life with cosmic light." he continued, "I bet Greppy Graviton has something to do with their Earthly existence, he'll ground anything of light he can get his tentacles on! How can that possibly be true?" It was in Elcy Electron's constitution to emit a negative charge at the end of all matters. "However a little understanding of worldly realm events and perhaps a visit into the Earthy dimension would do him well." Petky Proton thought to himself.

There was an internal grumble in Greppy Graviton's nucleus as he had overheard Petky's thought, and then he whipped past the present along the periphery of the future for temporary solitude.

Elcy Electron could make the other Children dizzy-wizzy because he constantly orbited their minds. He was relentless in his quest to keep the nuclei of their inner worlds in a spindle! Elcy Electron perched on his own receptors when a petty push morphed into a galactic shove from the others, whereas the Children were content to simply chill elsewhere during his shifting tides. When Elcy was disillusioned by the Children's reactions he begrudgingly gave them quantum-slack. He instinctually knew if they *high-tentacled-it* out of his field, and took a hiatus in outer-dimensional space, he would vanish into oblivion. Elcy could not exist without the other Children, and neither could the Earth realm.

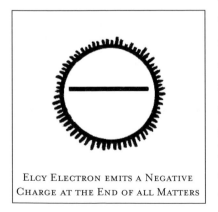

ELCY ELECTRON EMITS A NEGATIVE CHARGE AT THE END OF ALL MATTERS

Neppy Neutron examined Elcy from a distance and accumulated his essence of solitary calmness. Neppy was usually in an explosive mood.

He had made stellar strides in previous continuums to learn how to recalibrate his thoughts without blasting off to the others. However, they accepted him and his constitution. The rest of the Children never had any quirks or quarks about his outbursts. They knew what to expect and he never strung them along, especially between dimensions.

NEPPY NEUTRON'S NEWLY-CLEAR THOUGHTS

Neppy Neutron processed his newly-clear thoughts as he dropped into his own powerful center. He carefully attuned his antennas in an upright position, three octaves higher for optimum reception. Neppy Neutron ingeniously fired off creative sparks to the others, who formed ideas that were amplified and broadcast into the atmosphere. Instinctually he was a great concept molecule — a heck of a bright Neutron that Neppy was. He then transmitted his thoughts on the matter to GrandPa, who said,

"Color feeds the desire to create and is part of the energy that is carried in light from the Sun — a celestial star that is also reflected in the hearts of Humankind. Humans are animated beings of light who absorb the nourishing frequencies of the colors carried in the Sun's light and are held in form through the configuration of Phi."

The Particles, or the Waves, were drawn into realms of relativity. When the Particles arrived on the spinning disk for the story, they were punctual and direct whereas the light Waves were drearily nuclei-eyed. The Waves constantly viewed illusionary worlds at an angle. "However," GrandPa advised the rest of the Children, "never let the precipitating Particles of reality, nor their accomplice, the wandering Waves of emotion, slip by unnoticed, as they have something to share like the rest of you. Although the Waves lack substance and the Particles can appear to be quite pushy, their struggle in opposition will keep you on your tentacles." They could never see nucleus-to-nucleus on anything, except at zero point. The Earthly world saw life through three-dimensional spectacles and it was viewed as either a Particle or a Wave and never the two as a whole.

"Assemble yourself and become apparent," pleaded the Particle to the Wave. "Shift within the cosmic tides or we may part ways," whaled the Wave, as he propelled into the next time continuum. It was their fate to be together forever. They were one and the same with different perspectives. The wandering Waves reunited after their cosmic swim. Sighing blissfully as feelers interlocked with the ever-supportive Particles, they melded together on a tangerine and lemon light-beam.

THE PARTICLES AND THE WAVES DRAWN INTO REALMS OF RELATIVITY

"Looks like a dust storm on the horizon." charged the Electron Elcy, as a sandy mist moved overhead.

"Hey Dudey Dust, dust off the atmosphere and settle down for a change," Neppy Neutron said knowingly. He knew Dudey was showing off his mystical powers with his slate-of-tentacles routine to impress GrandPa. GrandPa just absorbed all the energy emissions from the Children and transmuted it into playful dream stuff.

DUDEY DUST SETTLING DOWN

Well, dubious Dudey Dust knew his calling in the Universe as he tended to drift into the others' dreamscapes when he was creatively stirred, and then, unfortunately, he became scattered. Dudey cascaded and faded in and out of realities whenever it suited him. He spent many moons constructing the frameworks of future storylines. "How do you think all of those celestial bodies formed in the cosmos?" teased GrandPa, "Worldly realms would not be the same without Dudey Dust." he mused, in an overtone of gold and silver threads, laced with sapphire flecks. The Children gleefully laughed and swirled, creating funnels of color energy. They jumped in, slid about, and spun around these funnels. They were having a grand time and sang so sweetly,

"Dudey, Dudey, Dudey stardust oh so bright,
Give us the reign of the cosmos, and we'll give you matter of light "

Dudey smirked and repositioned his Particles of light to welcome the jingle. He knew how important stardust was to Creation. GrandPa depended on Dudey Dust to transport his concepts and actions to Earth. Greppy Graviton had arrived back hipping-and-blopping onto the disk. He was always digesting and assimilating the lighter side of life on his path as he blipped bubbles of dust.

Greppy Graviton firmly supported Alte Atom, who was full of zest, as he flittered and darted away. He was in continual orbit of this present reality's evolutionary cycle. Excited about the upcoming expansion plan, he zipped and zoomed across the ionosphere until he found a place to alight and attempted to listen patiently to the story's unfoldment. Restless once again, he dashed after his thoughts to keep up with himself.

GREPPY GRAVITON

Greppy Graviton reflected inwardly, "Alte Atom had the ability to alter nothingness into somethingness with all his bopping about, whereas Dudey Dust helped Greppy repair the fragile structures that constantly collapsed as matter formed. A firmer foundation was required in order for reality to exist. However, all of the Children, including himself, accepted this chaos as part of the long-term agenda of the Voice."

The Voice had been tuning into the conversation and brightly burst in and then disappeared back into oblivion, leaving a trail of stardust that carved out this hieroglyphic key — revealed only to GrandPa's inner sight,

"Don't you agree, the Children are a mysterious group of alchemists who are also on a journey. They have unlimited futuristic and ancestral traits that cosmically continue to be refined as they unravel their timeless riddles and rhymes. They are tricksters and chameleons of space in any continuum. In the center of each and every one of the Children, their replicates, and descendants, are codes of mystical universal powers. The group will become a single force of nature and transform into the Pioneers' alchemical reservoir. When all unite and are brought into full registration, they will provide unlimited magical possibilities for Humankind. A cosmic treasure chest if all goes according to plan."

GrandPa illuminated with this possibility and merged his consciousness within his emerald-rose heart, as he clicked forward the cosmic dial of the story.

The galactic Pioneers were on a quest
as the violet ray faded upward.
The Children dipped down an octave,
to surf the indigo ray of the story.
GrandPa observed.
The Voice directed.
Hold the sapphire scepter close to Heart.

Chapter Two

Wisdom and knowledge containing elements of Breath
Imagination opening across the vast horizons that lay outstretched
Its secrets imploding and exploding within the time-space continuum
Guised as sister, brother, mother, father, all kin

— Indigo

The Children of the Multiverse formed a sphere and orbited around GrandPa above the floating disk. Intuitively, they knew this was much more than a once upon a time story, as it was a legendary space odyssey that occupied all intergalactic space in the time continuum of Earth.

"Drop into your imagination and become part of its evolutionary spin in a whirlwind of light." said GrandPa as he continued, "Since its inception, that sparked during a cosmic breath, it has remained activated by osmosis for all to view. A single cosmic breath is one explosive bang in a series. It's designed as a cyclical expansion process of creation."

"We will need to unwind the colossal cosmic clock back to the story's genesis with its exact star coordinate. The position of the cosmic dial on the clock is paramount for the universal mirror to appear before us." GrandPa whispered as he watched the Children perk up.

THE COLOSSAL COSMIC CLOCK

"We'll be able to clearly see the reenactment of the journey by its mirror reflection in playback motion. We will discover how life on Earth was animated in a spectacular way by the Phi-ionospheres, which, of course, is our group of seven photonic space travelers."

GrandPa began to televise the clock's outward projector as linear time clicked into forward play. The Children focused their attention on the universal mirror, in awe of its captivating imagery in motion.

The Phi-ionospheres held the mighty sapphire scepter to lead the way on their space travels. The scepter contained the magical cosmic force of the ionosphere which was the outer energy field surrounding the Earth. Miracles are felt by those who feel the wisdom and knowledge coded within the sapphire scepter. To conceal their powers and protect them from evil forces, the Phi-ionospheres traveled secretly as Pioneers, their space alias. To the Voice this group of seven would always be his light-swashing, color-buckling wizards of light.

GrandPa hit the pause button, turned and transmitted to the Children, "You have great alchemical influences on Humankind and are the keys that activate the Pioneers' dreams into real time experience. But first, let me tell you about your genesis in the cosmos. This next scene on screen concerns Subbie Consciousness, who is not only the

Voice's counterpart, but who is also your cosmic mother. Let's take a closer look at her story."

The universal mirror magically transformed into a motion picture outlining the genesis of all life which awoke within a spark of inspiration in Galaxy Siptrom's 49th Dimension. Subbie Consciousness gazed intently at her hazy reflection blossoming in the looking glass. The Voice had given her independence and she reigned over her own cosmos eons from his cosmic realm in space. Her likeness shimmered and became a silhouette. Quite intrigued with her silhouette, something had shifted in her mind and felt ladylike, but that couldn't possibly be. With that thought she morphed from an edgeless being to a shape and was startled by her shape-shifting transformation. She fell forward, then ricocheted off the looking glass and spiraled out of the Siptrom's infinite bandwidth. Subbie was zapped into a black hole never to be seen again in this dimension. This unruly outburst nearly shattered the colonies of the stellar neighborhood.

"Galaxy Siptrom's loss was Planet Earth's future gain." GrandPa added as he hit the pause button, "Let me explain this a little further as all of you Children are the *'Aspects of Reality'* or *Earth life's chemical composition.* In that infinite flash, subtle tones and nuances were unleashed from within the looking glass. All life is either reflected outward as visible matter or deflected inward and hidden from sight. Both sides exist depending upon your perception. And collectively you are the components that will create the formula of life-pattern sequences." continued GrandPa. "Your role in the magnification and colorization of illusion will unfold through life on Earth, when you connect with Subbie and remember what occurred at that moment when she disappeared."

The Children deciphered and decoded each sound telepathed by GrandPa. In a zippity-zappity-zoop they quickly resettled and snuggled close. They interlocked into each other's fibrous hairs as they began to decipher the patterns of the mind map program for this mission.

"The Pioneers will depend on you to interact and to support physical and chemical processes through seven separate energy centers found in Humans. The energy centers are similar to the interplanetary switching stations that you installed and implemented in the 11th Dimension of the Galaxy Ganglion." GrandPa reminded them as he slid deeper into his crystalline ruby cushion and observed the Children charging up. Their curiosity sparked at each word he transmitted.

GrandPa inspired the Children with the following verse,

"My heart is a tremendous transformer and bubbles over with the mysterious secrets of this Universe for those who listen. When on Earth be still and listen to the whisper of the heart."

GrandPa gazed upward. The skies were illuminated with streaks of blue and flecked with yellow hues. Peach, pink and crimson swirls of energy swiftly spun alongside the rim of the golden disk. The silence of stillness crept over the skies. The Heavens flung open once again.

The Voice parted the clouds with his Presence and inscribed the following message across the horizon. Each word was thoughtfully carved into and permeated the ethers. It read:

*"Energy treads before fleeting feelings of inspiration,
Collective consciousness of Humankind will undergo transformation,
The revelation and knowing of self through its galactic Pioneers
will assist to transform rigid belief systems and patterns of fears."*

A sudden explosive bang was sounded and rattled the Children's spinning disk. Instantaneously all letters shattered into countless stardust smithereens. This particular bang's genesis originated in the 12th Dimension. The Voice routinely parted the Heavens with his breath of smokeless fire for a closer peak. Each dimension of space lifted to unveil colossal stellar structures that were shattered by the boom's vibrations bouncing off intergalactic bodies. It had a domino

effect. Galaxies disintegrated leaving behind a vast velvety space of saddened darkness. The Angelic Realms' high-pitched sounds echoed in eternity, alerting and motioning the Galactic Guzanard Guard (GGG). Chaotic turbulence could be manipulated by the GGG to bring interdimensional space back into order. However, the GGG knew this was a task for the Voice. The Voice knew everything that occurred in his Metaverse, which

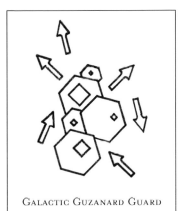

GALACTIC GUZANARD GUARD

encompassed everything conceivable before the next bang ever boomed. It was all prerecorded and only the Voice and Subbie knew the program code, as they created it together. The Voice gathered momentum with a zap and a zoom, then zipped up the Heavens behind him.

"Well, now," GrandPa paused while he gazed around. He inconspicuously shook his ethereal presence. He then proceeded to smooth down his rattled rhithers and tattered thithers into a quieter style. "Now that's a blustery solar storm!" he said, as he switched on the projector, "Where was I, oh yes, our Pioneers were also influenced and thrown off course. The Voice will return to check on the Pioneers on the other side of the mirror soon. Now adjust your radar and tune into the universal mirror in front of you. Observe the Pioneers' spacecraft as it swishes about in outer space at the beginning of this journey."

The Pioneers were on track when the explosion rocketed their spacecraft into an unchartered black hole. It swooped off its plotted course, spiraled, and in a catastrophic spindle, spun and then totter-teetered. Little did they know that the blast was a cosmic inbreath and would repeat itself at random as its part of the cosmic expansion program. Its outbreath created a sudden jolt and redirected the craft off course once again. Second in Command Pioneer Illepio Indigo reprogrammed the navigation server. They spliced and sliced through many dimensional gridlines and crosspoints. The momentum of the craft slowed down as it chugged between the dodging remnants and debris of shattered galaxies. The GGG reported it would take a kavillion phi-light years for space to recalibrate and stellar structures to self-repair. However, the Voice would take care of it.

Space had buckled and created a warp in the timeline. The craft wobbled into a sideward spiral and then swerved into position. It gently landed on top of the displaced stellar debris. The shaky debris rocked and swayed from the chaotic energy forces still at large. First in Command Pioneer Veteko Violet cracked open the lever panel and

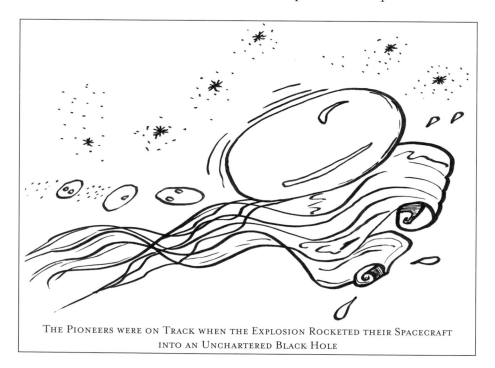

THE PIONEERS WERE ON TRACK WHEN THE EXPLOSION ROCKETED THEIR SPACECRAFT INTO AN UNCHARTERED BLACK HOLE

peered out into the darkness of space. Space was her home and she was the leader on this escapade.

In sequence all seven Pioneers fired-off their receptors as they disembarked, led by Veteko with the sapphire scepter held high in her antenna. She had seen many galaxies and been thrown about by countless cosmic bangs of breath, but for some strange vibration, she felt her resonance and that of her spacemates were about to change in the near future. She passed on instructions to Pioneer Fifth in Command Yegerte Yellow. It would take Yegerte's expertise to recalibrate the spacecraft's travel program before they set back out on course. It seemed like an eternity in the universal mirror, but it was just a cosmic flash.

Once they retuned to their extraordinary senses, each one carefully stretched and twisted their luminous forms back into respectable shape. In unison they jointly sparked and twinkled in a beautiful array of shimmering colors and sent out a flare to alert the GGG that all was okay.

"Galactically known as the unsinkables," interrupted GrandPa excitedly and continued, "these beacons of light surfed the cosmic waterways of space. Since the inception of creation they were on an eternal quest influencing immeasurable cosmic breaths and illuminating new galaxies along the space grids."

These unsinkable Pioneers had sailed across many worldly realms. They observed star wars, cracked open stargates, relocated portals and programmed syntax keys — all to satisfy their longing to unfold the plan of evolution. Trekking across time-space continuums they rode waves of alternating current. When on land, direct current energy was desired to securely affix their grounding cords to land. This was necessary as they required a direct link to a celestial body's central source. Direct current reservoirs were positioned throughout intergalactic switching stations for planetary and stellar terrain expeditions.

This inquisitive team was adventurous and eager to discover outer-worldly conditions, habitats and life forms. All destinations plotted had landing pads and adaptable terrains where they could set up camp. They constructed solid ground for their camp sites by condensing energy that moved at very slow rates of vibration. When the team was charged up and well calibrated from their intergalactic break and had floated back into the spacecraft, Veteko secured the safety lever, flicked forward the control panel into position and proceeded to respond to umpteen telepathic broadcasts recorded on the Monitor. The Pioneers activated their phi-light panel to facilitate communications. It kept them in tune with their colleagues and friends.

Space travelers had such hectic, busy existences and chaotic odysseys lately. After all the messages were answered, Yegerte collapsed the transmission of the conversation structure to prevent it from propelling into alternating timelines for infinity.

Energy treads before thought mapping outlines of events that adhere to the cosmic space recorder forevermore. It was highly recommended by the Galactic Council to wipe your blackboard clean during all space travel. Some travelers forgot and their recorded messages or adventures continuously replayed for eternity when a resonate situation was sounded in the cosmos.

The group adhered to the *Cosmic Code of Conductivity*. They never left a mess of superfluous energetic debris all over space, as it could create future chaos as space was originally created with order in mind. When Humankind is enlightened, they will also be careful of indelibly outlining events or of leaving behind energy patterns for others to become entangled in.

Veteko switched off the bandwidth station and disengaged the telechannel. All systems were online as she fired up the craft. The Pioneers were prepared for take-off. They headed in the direction of the final destination point plotted on their map; known as Salunken the Sun, a radiant celestial star they had waited eons to explore. They puttered off into the darkness leaving behind a trail of rainbow bubbles that soon evaporated into oblivion.

The indigo ray swerves upward
to introduce the descent of the next octave,
the blue ray.
Explore the personalities and traits
of the seven colorful Pioneers.
Introduce yourself as
the Children did.
They are all unique and also part of you.

CHAPTER THREE

The rattle, a roll and sputtering of the spoken word
At time, All wondering if this is not absurd
If essence can blurt the nothingness with just a mutter
Sounds can digitally become apparent in a flash with thunder

— Blue

A sense of eeriness lurked in outer space. Silence echoed as it filled the void and stilled the energy flow of its cosmic waters. The Pioneers detected an unidentified vibration that stirred in its depths. The mighty ones knew something was brewing and adjusted their x-ray visors and sensor scopes. They buckled themselves in their silk-like restrainers, made of molded emerald space matter, and then spun-off in their spacecraft and swerved along its unidirectional path. To build momentum, they swayed in and grooved out of nebulae and interplanetary dust. They were phi-light years ahead of their rivals — the Wiggly Wickochettes, but in sight on their detection module.

The notorious Wickochettes had plotted the exact coordinates of the invincible Pioneers for eternity. Their mission was to conquer the sapphire scepter for their own use in the underworldly realms. These realities were dark and evil and could only be accessed through the vacuum of specific black holes in space. Both in interstellar and interplanetary spaces, they took great pleasure stirring up cosmic havoc as they marveled in destroying meteoroids, rearranging asteroids and flinging around comets into neighboring galaxies. The GGG had pinned them down in outer space during their last expedition, but they were quick to hide out of their radar range within the tenuous plasma of intergalactic crevices. The Voice had carefully charted the complete odyssey at the beginning of time to avoid any accidental surprises, which could create turbulent cosmic waters to overflow.

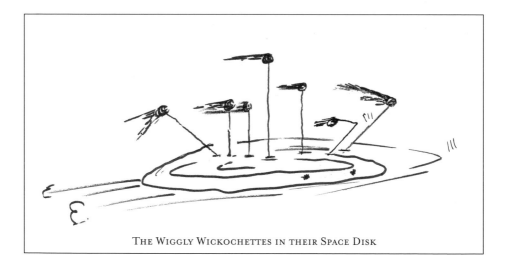

THE WIGGLY WICKOCHETTES IN THEIR SPACE DISK

In a quantum leap, the stick-like nonsentients saw the cosmic window of opportunity in time and popped through it. The Wickochettes were now cruising along the Pioneers' grid way as planned. Being in their euphoric gaseous state, they did not detect the approach of the Voice's cosmic force on their radar. As they closed in on the bubble trail of the Pioneers' craft, the Voice glimpsed down at their space disk and at warp speed, swatted them with his breath and swept them into oblivion.

The sudden jolt created static turbulence and Veteko quickly reset the spacecraft's Gridometer. They snapped back onto the grid and continued calmly on course. Veteko was always on full alert even when outer space appeared to be in order. The craft puttered along and slightly skidded as it skimmed off a patch of slippery tachyon space plates and inadvertently spun over a series of stargate crossings. They could sense they were very close to their destination.

To alert the attention of space travelers in close proximity, distant stars sparkled. The space ways buckled under the pressure of the uninhabited stars' loneliness. The stars possessed an inner flame of desire that burned incessantly. They had their own agenda which was to be discovered. They dazzled travelers with such starshine that even the galactic Pioneers and the Wiggly Wickochettes were starstruck. Excitedly, the stars dreamed of voyagers trekking across their bodies of eternal light. Each had a reflective mandate and a desire to be the brightest scintillation in their constellation, as coded in their blueprint. A conglomerate of stellar structures from an outer dimension heard their wishes. They shimmered as the stars swayed, then gracefully bowed through to their dimension and offered kind words for the stars' heartfelt requests.

"Sweet little stars of light,
Don't be sad, the cosmos will make it right,
Your essence will be discovered when your time is ripe,
The Voice will gift you with eternal inner sight."

The resonance of hope echoed in the core of the innocent starlets. The conglomerate televised Pioneer Fourth in Command Gerpy Green to plot the stars' coordinates in his navigation recorder. Through stellar visits, the Pioneers supported stars who were ready to cluster into constellations.

GrandPa hit the pause button on the universal mirror and captured an image frame of a radiant orange sphere. GrandPa sent out his molecules of light to gather information about the Pioneers and to introduce them to the Children. Expanding his consciousness outward, he spoke: "The group of seven may be the unsinkable photon team in outer space, but on Earth all are distinct and each will possess planetary elements indigenous to Earth. Each one is a quantum orb of visible light colored with particle-wave properties and cosmic radiation."

"They exhibit individuality and exist collectively to reflect the evolution of life. Instinctually, each identifies with their color frequency. During the shifting of cosmic currents, their size and the mass of their wavelength expands and stretches to the outer limits of intergalactic space. Being in an elastic state allows them to explore simultaneous dimensional realities. While on Earth the Pioneers will be less pliable and will need to consciously hold themselves in place to avoid disintegration. Each Pioneer symbolizes a negatively or positively charged energy form, setting his or her character attributes in motion. As their quantum somatic insights evolve while on Earth, they will modify their electromagnetic charge with the polarity shifts, keeping in rhythm with the Human oscillating process."

Pioneer Sixth in Command Orenga Orange gleamed as he subtly overheard GrandPa. He wildly poked through a crack in the reflection of his frozen image in the mirror and stared directly at GrandPa atop his ruby cushion. Orenga smirked at him, teasingly wiggling his form and waving his antenna at the Children. He swiveled around in the spacecraft and winked at his spacemates, then slipped back through the crack to the deflective side of the universal mirror to rejoin them.

Surprised at Orenga's unexpected visit to his realm, GrandPa checked the cosmic dial as the crossover juncture became visible on the story gridmap. Absolute time was beginning to buckle and bend in anticipation of the Children's visit. The cosmic clock struck 11:11 as the motionless picture of Orenga's nucleus struggled to shift form in the mirror. GrandPa hit the play button, and Orenga joyfully whipped around in the mirror as the rest of the Pioneers began to vibrate and align into their respective sequence to be introduced. The Children giggled as GrandPa spoke intently,

"Seventh Pioneer in Command is Regeta Red. Regeta not only has the longest wavelength of his team but his strength fires up and stimulates thought waves into action, propelling them forward with positive force in the expansion plan. With an unlimited resource of magnetic radiation he'll ignite experiential dreams into full activation." Being a passionate and hot photon with strong gravitational pressure, Regeta was influential in rooting life into many galaxies. When the spaceways became cluttered with debris and matter, Regeta teleported into the past, then to the future and back again, radiating coherent beams of red to influence various timelines. He disintegrated stagnate gaseous formations and tenuous plasma making way for unimpeded travel. Driven by determination, he dimensionally demonstrated an

REGETA RED AND YEGERTE YELLOW
IN THE UNIVERSAL MIRROR

insatiable desire to cocreate realities and firmly ground them within worldly realms.

Next is Orenga Orange. "We recently met Orenga, the quantum of visible orange light, in the universal mirror exhibiting his magical sense of humor!" GrandPa laughed quietly and continued, "Being the creative reservoir of the spectral team, Orenga has an innate ability to tap into his imagination and manifest innovative ideas and universal concepts. Having properties of joyfulness and playfulness, he will be a great inspiration for all life on Earth by supporting them with his encouraging positive mind map system. Orenga cheerfully participates in the outer galaxy's evolutionary process, as he emits magnetic radiation that can spark the genesis of creation into form. The orange frequency animates life for colonization on many intergalactic planetary systems."

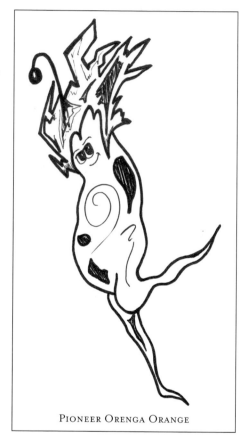

PIONEER ORENGA ORANGE

"Next in order of color wavelength is Yegerte Yellow. Yegerte demonstrates rational strength which augments his technical cosmic mindset. He is magnetically charged to recalibrate and adjust galactic space systems. Although Yegerte is a shorter wavelength than Orenga — all Pioneers' responsibilities rank equally in a quantum existence. Yegerte supports his team with wit, cleverness and ingenuity and is the intellectual source for the group. The yellow radiance of his personality can purify thought and the memory prints of timelines. When a dark dust belt becomes unstable, in the midst of turmoil, Yegerte can absorb, digest and transform frenzied frequencies with yellow undertones into currents of tranquility. He'll undertake preventative measures to energetically flush out mind patterns that coast in cosmic waterways. He will be a great warrior of emotions in flux that will be felt and experienced in his future home on Earth." GrandPa added.

"For equilibrium, Gerpy Green is positioned as the center field frequency of visible light and retains the team's balance of opposing electric and magnetic forces. Gerpy self-correcting equilibrium emanates the quintessence of love for the full spectrum. Even the wicked Wiggly Wickochettes' nuclei are spark-shocked by the vibration of Gerpy's light. Being a sensitive photon, he will be somatically in touch with and will photosynthesize nature on Earth in conjunction with the Sun. Galactically known as a harmonic interface, he will instill balance in all space matters. Gerpy oscillates alongside the electrically-charged Pioneers, but occasionally swings towards the magnetic pull of the spectral team. However, he is considered a neutral photon and is respected by all space nations due to his gentle emissions of kindness that can open stargates for intergalactic diplomacy. He acts as a conduit for the vibrations of life to travel upon and brings peace and harmony to startled and lonely stars in newly forming constellations. Gerpy can create calmness and will address the havoc that erupts on Earth. He will serve as the team's equalizer when their electricity and magnetism is separated by the shifting of the Earth's poles. Gerpy will readjust the poles to their proper longitudes and stabilize the orbital wobble of the Earth's inner core."

The projector emitted blue noise signaling the channel to focus on the next Pioneer. "Gliding along to the opposite side of the spectral team are cooler Pioneers who are electrically charged. Third in Command Pioneer Betern Blue is a shorter wavelength than Gerpy and

communicates with finesse. She is the bridging station for interplanetary and interstellar relations and processes the codes on Veteko's
Calometer, the intelligent radio receiver. She is knowledgeable in the
field of galactic affairs and calibrates and telepaths to the other
Pioneers. In her future role on Earth, she will personalize her sonic
expressions with verbalized sound projections creating language. Betern
also transmits emissions into the synaptic junctions of the Galaxy
Ganglion's 11th Dimension, in order to examine spatial growth. Gerpy
assists Betern on this plane as its colonies' electrical systems exhibit
erratic nervous behavior."

"Illepio Indigo, energetically aligned to Betern, is patient by nature
but flares in astonishment when Betern's telepathic transmissions zoom
ahead to explore unassigned stargates, whereas Illepio prefers to silently
reflect and evaluate these coordinates before switching course. She
believes there is all the space in the cosmos to explore, so why race
against the winds of scalar waves? Illepio is smart and has the capacity to
stimulate the mind into activation while implementing the creative
process of the others. Guided by her innate intuition, Illepio's electric
indigo energy soars beyond her awareness and unilaterally triggers
further expansion of the evolutionary cycle. Not only is her thought
process incredibly swift, but with Veteko's direction, she can also
configure sine waves into activity. The Voice's broadcasts keep Illepio's
focus on a selected track of the cosmic recorder, as she is the vibratory
antenna that deciphers and codes communication networks in space."

Veteko Violet regally wafted up to the universal mirror, as GrandPa
winked, "Veteko is the coolest wavelength and she exists by the strength
of her violet attributes. She has accessed ultraviolet and microwave
radiations to enhance communication, and has obtained the highest
amplitude on her team. For convenience, the two systems are linked
into her Calometer. Veteko radiates a sense of confidence and being a
leader of galactic travelers, she mesmerizes all who enter her field with

her electric charisma. She is detail-oriented and even a black hole void can't slip by her unnoticed."

"Although she may be the shortest wavelength, her electrifying personality would not only knock an antenna into orbit, but would melt a nucleus into nothingness if that were her decision. Magically, she can distill the resonance of space debris and disintegrate matter with the helical wave of a tentacle. She is First Pioneer in Command through the virtue of her wisdom and was crowned by the Galactic Council for her ability to electrify bolts of violet light." said GrandPa as he gulped. Veteko's presence energetically captured GrandPa's breath.

He caught his fleeting breath, descended down a few notches to an alternative octave and continued, "The group will bring extraordinary psychological and therapeutic powers from their respective colors to Earth. They will adapt to the tides of human emotion and personify these colorful feelings as experiences. Humans will also discover how to tap into their own extraordinary powers through these magical colors."

"Okay, try not to confuse me GrandPa," Neppy Neutron blasted, as he took note with his twisted tentacles. The rest of the Children grinned and then tuned their attention tracks back onto the story. They all knew that he was not a mild-mannered molecule, but neither were they for that matter. GrandPa nodded and switched the projector to the bandwidth in time where he had freeze-framed the movie onto an alternate channel.

The story fast-forwarded to the scene coordinate where the spacecraft was just about to float smoothly and entwine within numerous timelines in dimensional space. Then every moment seemed to interpenetrate into another time frame as the universal mirror began to move faster than the speed of the Pioneers' light.

Veteko pondered quietly to herself. Her sensory receptors were alerted to observe unidentified outer forces. Perhaps the Wiggly Wickochettes reset their program back into her orbit she signaled to the others. Vector visions of being a static element, unable to move in a strenuous situation ran along her mind current. A mind wave of a terrain of muck took form and she then knew the cosmic dice would spin and go amuck. They were encircling the parabolic curve of an eon continuum and line coordinates were bending and buckling inward. Storylines in various levels of evolution had become entwined and tangled. It could create a very chaotic situation to unravel. She contacted the GGG and advised them of the circumstance.

The craft's Gridometer was sounded. It flashed and sparked colorful flares as it passed the final switching station into the next constellation. All systems shut down right on schedule as they arrived at their destination. They gently rocked and swayed their craft as it gently clicked down through stellar dust on the landing pad of its destination. This celestial star released his brilliance and lit up its navigational satellite. This made it easier for the Pioneers to hook onto the force field of this self-gravitating sphere. They landed without scorching a receptor or disturbing a tentacle. It was not just another victorious landing for the adventurous team, as they knew this was a very special journey but could not remember what the future had outlined for them in the cosmic expansion plan.

They unilaterally drifted out of the craft in sequence, escorted by Veteko who held the sapphire scepter high, as she peered over her antenna to see if they were being tracked. They descended onto the uncharted celestial body – a hydrogen and helium mass that glowed and radiated eternal power. It was given the name of Salunken the Sun by the Galactic Council. Salunken outshone many star clusters and planetary colonies. It was the first Sun implanted by the Voice within outer space and was the common center of gravity in its galaxy.

Salunken was known for nurturing planetary seedlings, for helping celestial starlings to emit light, and moons to reflect light in opposition. They were all raised into magnificent independent personalities. Some stars created their own constellations that will influence Earth forevermore. Salunken was given his very own solar system for his planets and moons to orbit in.

"As well, Salunken was kept in high regard amongst his intergalactic peers and kept Earth in orbit with the influential stellar and lunar cycles. Other stars visited from distant galaxies to see how Salunken's centripetal force influenced his celestial orbit. Star clusters from many dimensions dreamed of being his apprentice and would bring trace elements as offerings. He considered mentorship to be a great honor and cherished the trace elements by keeping them close to his center," informed GrandPa as he turned towards the mirror.

The team linked their receptors to Salunken and awaited a response signal. Salunken sent a violent explosion of gaseous flames outward from his surface as a welcoming solar salute. In an excited state a solar wind encircled the Pioneers' spacecraft and its gust nearly blew their antennas into disarray. Salunken signaled for them to create a camp beside the mighty pillar of light that rose from the most northerly curve along his spherical body. It was the perfect location and a magnificent haven with a view of the crystalline mountain, laden with precious gaseous gem drops. A second mountain towered by its side, its depth providing a shadow effect, a perfect setting to construct camp. The Pioneers' first priority was to clear superfluous static interference, and recharge and top up their energy levels. In a flash, they recalibrated as Regeta plotted the dimensional space required, and then they gathered together in a colorful orbital manner to begin.

In unison they entered an altered state of consciousness and collectively began to dream their camp into creation. Once the image took hold in their mind, they projected it outward as objects from the dreamscape. Powerful vision and intent sparked the construction process and set it into motion. Beams and boards were created from nebulous stardust forming their foundation on this glowing colossal sphere of light. Seven individual huts were created as each Pioneer had a specific color preference for their quarters. It was also a galactic requirement to bathe in their own frequencies during contemplation and growth continuums. The outer siding of each hut was made from solidified plasma, an iodized gas from Salunken. The inner walls were lined and laced with sparkling stardust to replicate that comfortable spacey feeling they were so accustomed to. They also erected a common meeting lodge where they could gather or just hover around carefree. They had a naming ceremony and called their camp, Plaxo. Salunken nearly burst his crust in glory as he sent out a solar flare.

The Pioneers reigned on Plaxo for eons. The terrain of Salunken was an oasis of countless flowing rivers, deep waterways and lush natural colors. A place of beauteous wonder displaying crystalline structures of unique form, glistening in an endless array of colorful rainbows from red to violet, violet to red and Sun-like frequencies. Flickering flames danced in the solar light of Salunken's eternal flame. Yet its radiant glow was a smokeless fire. On occasion deeper fires roared and flared from the core of its being. It was toasty hot during every solar cycle, even when it had a solar snowstorm. There was so much to explore on Salunken. For their celestial celebrations, stellar, planetary and lunar personalities from the surrounding grids would visit Salunken's solar oasis.

Now Orenga was the party Pioneer. He nearly blew his photonic seams open as an idea sparked in his nucleus. He wanted to throw a galactic gala to remember. Ecstatically, he shared his thoughts with Regeta who was equally excited and who bubbled over at the possibility. Regeta relished in the existence of all life and its propelling motion.

They coordinated the extravaganza's logistics with Salunken and plotted a constellation map for their guests to navigate. Salunken loved space voyagers, especially an assortment of radiant personalities. Orenga was not only gutsy but he creatively designed a Salunkian decor that could throw a post-modern molecule into a frenzy. It was going to be the gala no one would ever erase from their memory banks. Salunken was thrilled as he tightened the photonic belt to contain himself.

Regeta and Orenga took turns sending out telepathic invitations throughout the multi-dimensional galaxies and beyond the periphery of outer space — and awaited signals of potential guests. Betern kept track of the guest list as it surpassed all dimensional expectations. Even the Angelic Realms replied and offered to perform their celestial tunes and to amplify the music of the spheres. Everyone knew this would be the largest gala in any Sun's existence and no life form would miss it for another world. The guest list included all neighboring extraterrestrials, as well as intergalactic sentient beings and nonsentients. It took *lots* of advanced planning to prepare such a colossal gala; guests would arrange to attend many phi-light years ahead and behind as all had very busy agendas. The Pioneers created space prints of the activities. The date was carved out, plotted on the grid and broadcast through the cosmic dial to get underway at 11:11.

The blue ray faded outward
and greeted the next octave with love.
Enter the harmonious green ray.
Join us all at the gala of the galaxies.
Be the galaxies.
Become the party.
Be part of its spectacular finale.

Chapter Four

The cosmic beat within heartfelt bliss
Fuels fires with a eternal luminous kiss
Cascading in rhythms imprinted within holographic reflection
Kaleidoscope mixes depict all possible keys for projection

— Green

"11:11 phi-light years had elapsed. Galaxies collapsed and rose as stellar structures swayed in excitement over their rebirth. The outline of the party had taken shape and was ready to blossom. A group of stars arranged themselves into a constellation becoming a map for the guests. The guests arrived at the registered star coordinates precisely at the same time. The cosmic scale tilted to one side from the weight of the guests causing the expansion plan to accelerate into activation. The tension escalated and echoed throughout outer space. A rumbling in its outer periphery sent out sensations of chaos in motion. The signal was ignored as the guests excitedly flocked towards Salunken. The gala of the galaxies took place right on dial and altered the Pioneers' existence forevermore," informed GrandPa to the anxious Children as they refocused their consciousnesses back into the universal mirror.

The seven Pioneers shimmered vigorously as sonic chimes welcomed the revelers. The team polished their photonic globules and illuminated their true colors to greet the swarms of intergalactic guests. Regeta had segregated the south-western side of Salunken as a landing pad for spacecrafts, travel boards, teleportation and bilocation cubicles. Yegerte kept order for landings, disembarkments from spacescrafts and teleportation sequences. Salunken was draped in the most exquisite array of color beams and bolts of gaseous formations.

Crystalline ruby structures were fashioned for the guests to congregate in. The guest list reached 144,000. Each guest was offered delectable delights and magical formulae to inspire them to play celestial board games, solar swings and slides. Orenga relished the festivity and ensured there were plenty of golden dance disks to float on. Colonies of sentient amebas jiggled and wiggled to the beat of the symphony of the spheres. The music echoed and ricocheted off distant stellar structures. It was tremendous fun as they escalated octave after octave in ecstasy. The sound created swirls of dancing colored spirals. Many colonies had an opportunity to catch up, nuclei-to-nuclei, on cosmic happenings. Suddenly, all sound came to a stop by the high-pitched shrill of intergalactic sirens.

Silence crept inward as the Angelic Realms detected a ripple in deep space. They embraced each other with unfolded wings as a mysterious current approached creating turbulent broadcasts that they were unable to identify.

Suddenly the cosmic clock came to a screeching halt as the celestial brake switched over. The revolutionary spin of its dial jolted and froze.

Gerpy harmoniously attempted to keep balance by adjusting the tension and equanimity. The erratic solar blast from Salunken's central core startled the guests and created a tumultuous cascading effect throughout the cosmos.

Yegerte encouraged the guests to back up their timelines in hope of recalibrating their original vibrations prior to the party. It was too late as the calamity was already imprinted in their gala outline. They braced for the shock that was gaining momentum and beginning to swell and expand the vastness of space. Gerpy irradiated a series of stellar explosions with beams of emerald light and rays of green and lemon flares. He could not unwind or calm the cosmic waters of this catastrophic event in motion, as it was already outlined, recorded for eons and being concurrently broadcast in alternating continuums.

"Why wasn't the blackboard in space wiped the last cyclical time it erupted?" fired off Neppy Neutron as he observed the chaos becoming fully charged into action.

"The Voice seldom erases adventure segments in his master plan. He delights in colorful scenes as colossal energy bands are built that he can use in other dimensions. Unless, of course, the Galactic Council suggests that he modify his plan for the benefit of future conditions or outcomes as part of the expansion plan. Let's watch and see what happens next." GrandPa said as he was also curious even though he had watched this story for many eons.

Salunken was out of control as his orbital spin ecliptically pattered and petered. It was a sad moment for Salunken. He began to choke and sputter thick blackened cosmic liquid. He experienced a catastrophic inner pressure and shot projectiles of gaseous fluid which overflowed and filled intergalactic spaces with gelatinous gunk. Forcing the scales of weights and measures to tilt, Salunken almost fell out of space through the vacuum of an unknown black hole. It was a gateway into oblivion. Veteko shook as the Wiggly Wickochettes' chilling sinister sneers echoed from deep within the abyss. But Veteko was quick to act. She and Illepio fired off electrical charges to irradiate and cool down the upsurge of Salunken's magnetic explosive force. They expanded their forms and wedged him between them to prevent him from being lured down into the Wickochettes' trap.

SALUNKEN WAS OUT OF CONTROL AS HIS ORBITAL SPIN ECLIPTICALLY PATTERED AND PETERED

"Where is the GGG when you need them?" panicked the Children. "Hush—hush. All is fine. It was their destiny and part of their evolutionary process." GrandPa reassured.

The party-amebas flipped, flopped and spun into intergalactic outer spaces. They rollied then pollied and tumbled. Others were heaved up and rocketed at supersonic speeds. Extraterrestrials from the Kapvon Galaxy in the 13th plane of existence soared to far-away constellations. They were thrown the greatest distance, possibly due to their spherical rocket-shaped figures. They catapulted and were slung out of control and splattered along the ten directional bands of the cosmos. Yet, they all made it okay.

Colonies from Galaxy Siptrom's 9th and 10th Dimensions, thirty-two units in total, were hurdled and propelled far and wide. It was quite a scene as they blasted off into oblivion in a stupor. They left electrifying streaks of gold, green, lavender and magenta in the darkness creating a cosmic tree-like impression in space.

To offer some twilight, neighboring stars twinkled in on the situation. There would not be much to tidy up, just some remnants of spacecrafts, clumped stardust debris, ameba splattering on the odd celestial body and gaseous spills to mop up.

"Now that's a party that no one will forget," the precipitating Particle said. "Salunken sure has a lot of explaining to do," the wandering Wave added as he drifted away.

GrandPa hit the pause button and said, "The assembly of guests had arrived from intergalactic realities in limitless dimensions. Their assemblage was a component of a greater purpose. The solar explosion was preplanned by the Voice to allow the Pioneers to be sling-shot into a new dimension."

All the Children began buzzing in disbelief. Alte Atom squealed and nervously began to replicate atoms all over the space. "The more the merrier for story time." the other Children thought.

A silvery-blue vortex spun in GrandPa's brow as he processed the event. He reassured the Children that all was well, as the guests remorphed to their original forms. GrandPa continued, "They were dispersed between inner dimensional spaces to colonize new galaxies and constellations as part of the expansion process. It was keyed into the master program and coded in nebulous space fibers."

The Voice had performed this event to the program's exact specifications with the exception of the splattered amebas. Random acts of free will consciousness were an aspect of the Voice's agenda and occurred when least expected. The amebas were prepared for their incarnation on another plane of existence. They were quite excited about their opportunity to evolve and transform into other lifeforms.

GrandPa solarized his extrasensory perception and said, "Children, recalibrate your senses, elevate your view up a few octaves and closely tune in with your senses." As GrandPa observed universal time clicking forward on the cosmic dial, he added, "Soon you'll become reacquainted with the Pioneers in their dimension and be the mystics that you always were. Never let your consciousness slip into a black hole and always stay connected to Subbie's source in the 49th Dimension." GrandPa reminded the Children as they tuned back into the universal mirror.

Space was silent and felt the void. In sadness, the stars hid their glitter in respect for Salunken, who was greatly disappointed as he had waited so long for the gala. The cosmos felt outshone by Salunken's explosive eruption and inconspicuously interrupted the silence with an innocent tiny breath that rippled gently through space gaining

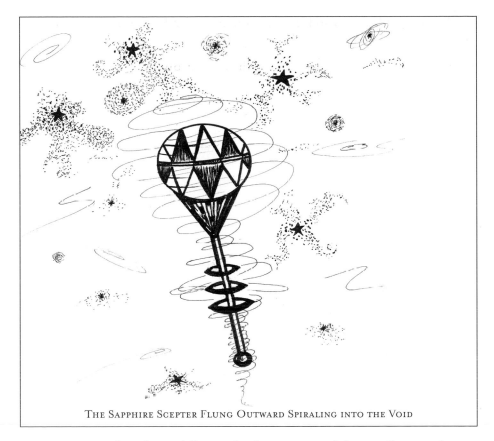

THE SAPPHIRE SCEPTER FLUNG OUTWARD SPIRALING INTO THE VOID

momentum — then boom! It smashed into space debris and created
turbulent chaos. Salunken quaked and wobbled then spun out of
control on his axis as his celestial cries were sounded, reverberating and
echoing throughout his galaxy.

The cosmos transmitted a formal apology to Salunken, but it was too
late for the Pioneers as they were launched off his surface and slung
into space in an uncontrollable solar fury. The stars created
constellations to assist the Pioneers' progress. Exact coordinates were in
full registration and the Pioneers were now on target towards Earth.
Veteko lost hold of her precious sapphire scepter as it flung outward
spiraling into the void. A glowing beam of indigo light dissipated into
the darkness as it vanished off Illepio's inner radar. She sensed it was
lost in outer space but not forevermore.

Salunken the Sun was heartbroken that they left so soon, especially without a proper farewell. He choked on tears of gaseous plasma that rolled out from his central core. Salunken decided he would enlighten the Pioneers — at least until they set up a new camp.

GrandPa reflected and concluded, "In fact, as the legend unraveled he radiantly fueled the Pioneers with solaristic power. Salunken was a wonderful father to Earth and her inhabitants. He shone incessantly and lit up her life both by day and by night. It was Humankind's perception of time that veiled night as a form of darkness, as Salunken the Sun never set, nor strayed from the hearts of Earth Humans.

The Voice materialized to ensure his entrance was televised on the universal mirror and gallantly swooped-up the group of seven in his cosmic force and positioned them upon the Salunkian galaxy's newest acquisition. They landed with a Plop! Bloop! Squish! Splat! Ooow! Kapoop! Boing! and careened onto a slippery landing pad.

The green ray dissipated
and in an upward spindle
opened the door of our next chapter:
the verse of the yellow ray,
the octave of intelligence and emotion.
Share its magnetic force
and its place on Earth.

CHAPTER FIVE

Free will creating interchangeable thoughts with actions
Transcribing into energy paths of emotional reactions
Infinite memory cranking out the process of expression
Unlimited possibilities for transformation or transgression

— Yellow

Smacken Krumple-Plop. Earth in her innocence wavered in anticipation of the Pioneers' arrival. Playfully, she tilted her body to and fro to welcome the newcomers. During her last evolutionary cycle, this visit was encoded on her celestial gridmap and scheduled for arrival at 11:11. To assist the Pioneers' descent she rotated to display the latitude and longitude of the most northeasterly point of her axis. Her childlike surge of excitement caused her terrain to buckle and create a concave trench on her outer crust.

"Ooops!" Earth apologized for an eruption on her dry and brittle surface. The Pioneers were her first galactic visitors and their inaugural drop landed them smack in a mound of muck gushing from her core. They flittered and fluttered then attempted to spring upward and spiral into a spindle. They could not move or budge in this matter. Although slightly perplexed they instinctually sensed Earth meant well as she didn't have a bad leyline circumnavigating her spherical body. The group tuned into each other's inner senses as they clumsily attempted to lift their photonic crystalline forms. The seven were immobilized as their receptor-transmitters were stuck within the clutches of her trenches. Betern's radio antenna wavered restricting a clear channel to alert the GGG for assistance.

A yellow-tangerine mist hovered over the terrain. The hazy mist extended as far as inner sight could decipher. They could have seen through many intergalactic dimensions from this angle with their sensor scope, but it had been left in the spacecraft on Salunken. The group reflected back to other exploratory odysseys. They were known as heroic photons who were famous for their precise blast-off and touch down techniques. The spacecraft's solar system program was based on an advanced galactic design. A signal was transmitted asking Salunken to teleport the craft at the next stargate opening.

Veteko led the group with her sensory receptors and approached the quandary from a different angle. She was a bright light and a quick quantum thinker, even during a standing wave or a wavering tide. She was swifter than cosmic lightning and mightier than the Mobile Multiwave Millicens, who were her allies in missions past. She adjusted her frequency in synchronization with the shifting colors of her team, snapped into her center and stilled herself for clear reception. She transmitted the incident to the Cosmic Council Helpline and received direct counsel. Veteko recorded the assignment code in her Calometer and acted promptly. She proceeded to reconnect her electrical system from alternating current to direct current. Veteko aligned to the Earth's energy field and locked into her gravitational force alongside her grid.

Veteko then lowered her cosmic pulse a few levels to register a harmonious inner beat with that of the Earth. This resonance was crucial for the mission to be successful and in accordance with the expansion plan. Earth jolted with the remembrance of her first helical breath of life. Memory recall patterns were triggered by electromagnetic charges circumnavigating her body.

The group followed Veteko's instructions in order of color sequence wavelength — Illepio was next in line and Regeta was the last. They easily reclaimed their light bodies from the muck, then scrubbed and polished them to a sparkling sheen and synchronized their systems to that of Earth. They relied on Veteko's expertise in challenging situations.

To collect themselves they reflected on energy patterns cascading in and out of Earth's universal consciousness and began to ride within her rhythmic dance until they reached a state of equilibrium. As GrandPa observed their reflective behavior in the universal mirror, he noticed that the wandering Wave took the initiative and slithered through the mirror to support the group's rhythmic calibration.

"Children, when the time is right, join the Wave in the story," GrandPa said. "We'd best catch up with him then," charged the precipitating Particle and Dudey Dust as they vanished into the mirror.

"I will assist as well," piped Greppy Graviton, knowing that the other Children would require his grounding force as long as eternity had an infinite plan and the constant desire to create animated form. He knew that the Pioneers required his presence to create the foundation for the remainder of the story. He playfully swept Dudey Dust along the Earth's barren playground. Dudey Dust giggled as he was delighted by Greppy's grounding moves.

Alte Atom buzzed excitedly as he rattled the spinning disk, and then disappeared through the mirror. He skidded and caught up to the Wave and the others. He knew he had a role to play in life's creation on Earth, as GrandPa smiled back at him through the mirror. The rest of the Children playfully popped in and out of Earth's worldly realm testing the cosmic waters and discovering their own mystical purposes.

Greppy Graviton secretly assisted the Pioneers to stay firm while oscillating within Earth's evolutionary frequency fluctuations. The jolt of rocketing off Salunken and aligning with Earth's vibration sent strange sensory shockwaves throughout the photonic cluster that opened gateways of emotional sensation. These energetically-charged sensations formed a range of feelings indigenous to Earth that acted like building blocks to support the illusion of human individuality.

Illepio felt a sense of comfort. She gazed up and felt Salunken, a solar light being, endlessly radiating support. She felt secure knowing that Salunken would watch over them for as long as they decided to stay on Earth.

The Voice flashed the legend forward to the next cosmic frame so he could make an appearance in the universal mirror. "Ah, he likes the big screen!" GrandPa chuckled to himself, and then spoke to the Children as they all gathered back on the disk.

"The Voice created this story for Human exploration and he will create other odysseys for future space travelers exploring evolutionary cycles. All Earthly possibilities reside within the Voice's mind." The Children closely watched the Voice on the universal mirror.

The Voice animated how charged imagery could create ideas in dimensional form. "Anything can materialize based on Humankind's perceptions." the Voice said as he stared directly at GrandPa and added,

"It will become common practice for Humankind to manifest universal mind patterns on Earth." And with that final vibratory thought, he vanished leaving behind a trail of white noise. GrandPa kept his visionary mind focused on the mirror as he continued,

"It was not programmed into the Pioneers' mind map to feel intense emotions or confusion in any given time continuum, or even on Earth, as it could affect the outcome of the story. However, as they acclimatized to Earth's vibrations at such an incredible rate, they were out of the program's control."

During these fluxuating intervals, they instinctively recalibrated to optimum function levels. They were feeling uneasy as they sensed the atmosphere surrounding Earth had a different sensation than other planets they had explored. It was fascinating to experience her physical impressions. They imprinted the patterns upon their sensory recorders for future reference and observation. Betern interpreted the distinctive Earthly codes and translated this information to the group. They were in awe by what they had discovered.

Regeta led the expedition on land while they explored uncharted territory. The team became responsive to the wide range of fragrances exciting their inner detection nodules. Cosmic rumor dictated that the sensation of fragrance evoked the human sense of smell. Managing to avoid olfactory overstimulation and maintaining a balanced photonic state on land, they were able to brilliantly light up Earth's blue powdered skies.

In a huff, the Calinger Clouds hastily moved in to investigate the commotion, and in hoping to draw the Pioneers' attention upward, outstretched her cloud span across the horizon. The group noticed her and sent colorful salutations. Exhilarated with the attention, she puffed out her fluffy-white chest and waved back. The Calinger Clouds absorbed the striking frequencies that pierced her mighty belly of fluffy stuff. Elatedly, she magically created a spectacle for all. As she started to joyfully cry, gaseous water droplets rolled down through the skies and splattered on Earth.

THE CALINGER CLOUDS' TEARS OF JOY

Gerpy squinted as the teardrops landed on his antenna. The Calinger Clouds teasingly blurred his inner vision to get attention. "Hey lady, don't cry, we'll play with you," the group radiated outward, and filled her chest with every color they could imagine and orchestrate. The group spun a mixture of gases into an orderly sphere and transformed it by beaming their frequencies — into a rainbow!

The Calinger Clouds almost fell out of the sky as her underpinnings loosened from her tears of joy. The Voice appeared in the mirror and with a single swoop, gently scooped up the Calinger Clouds and resuspended her on a higher dimensional octave. He then spliced the lower half of the spherical rainbow and hid it, along with its universal mysteries, within the underworld beneath the Earth. The Pioneers knew that an opportunity would arise for the two halves of the rainbow to reconnect and reveal their hidden truth. The Voice then vaporized into a misty swirl and vanished.

As Gerpy roamed, a surge of emptiness filled him with Earth's desire to transform into an enlightened planetary body. Earth, her future inhabitants and its vegetation, had so many possibilities available to them. Gerpy televised potential picturesque visions of Earth's

GERPY GREEN TELEVISED PICTURESQUE VISIONS

transformation into a natural beauty of color. Earth was thrilled with the possibilities and began to rotate and spin with hope.

The group sensed the Earth's shift was a signal to begin their explorations. They gathered in sequence with Regeta taking the lead. Not being in a physical form designed for this planet, it was a challenge for them to scurry rather than to float along. Veteko monitored the overall conditions on her Calometer and informed the Galactic Council of their findings. The colorful photonic chain chugged along Earth as they received messages from futuristic animal, plant, mineral, air and water kingdoms requesting to inhabit Earth's playground in living color.

Regeta's strong vibration of determination and will power set his team ablaze; it was a form of galactic encouragement and he truly enjoyed blazing new trails. He had an affinity to anchor higher frequencies during land expeditions. He also had the capacity to increase the circulation and speed of the team once they picked up momentum. Orenga sparked creative orange-filled ideas all over Earth as he jiggled merrily along behind Regeta. Yegerte, who had the ability to calm the erratic emotions of Earth, focused on his new surroundings, clumsily stumbled and bounced off the edges of a lifeless tree. He then splattered on top of a pile of jagged rocks and shattered into smithereens.

"Yegerte are you okay?" Gerpy said, as he swept up the pieces of Yegerte's scattered yellow and gold tidbits. Gerpy had been right on Yegerte's trail. Magically, he remolded the photonic mass back into form with a little space putty and gently placed Yegerte's nucleus back into position. Yegerte sparked and instantly recalibrated.

Gerpy was just being his nurturing loving self. He preferred to be in a harmonious state whenever possible. Knowing that Yegerte was back on grid, Gerpy twirled and sprung up in the air, with a bounce and a bound, radiating his healing qualities and trooped on.

YEGERTE YELLOW SPLATTERED ON TOP OF A PILE OF JAGGED ROCKS

BETERN'S ETHEREAL BLUE FORM LIFTED AND DRIFTED AWAY FOR A MOMENT

Betern trudged slowly along and sadly thought, "To get trapped in the trench can spin any photon off course." The Moon waxed and waned to deflect Betern's sorrowful feelings. Finally, Betern's ethereal blue form lifted and drifted away for a moment to reflect while gathering her vocal senses. The wandering Wave joined her as he didn't want her to travel too far in this transformative state.

Illepio and Veteko observed their images being reflected in a murky pond when they heard their vibratory notes being sounded and gazed up to the skies. It was their cosmic call to action. They alerted their team and all seven merged together.

They detected a presence in their dimensional space that had suddenly vanished, leaving a vibrational outline of children. Adjusting their antennas, they lingered waiting for a signal. They were mystified as all antennas began to vibrate and receive transmissions from inner space. They were tapping into seven extraordinary senses. Curiously, they wondered where they came from.

Distracted by a GGG signal that entered his energy field, Regeta wandered from the group to reorient himself. He had picked up that a force was approaching from the North, the South, the East and the West. The four directional winds of the Universe were moving inward with great pressure. Earth brought her orbit to a stop and braced herself. A great storm emerged from the Heavens above, or was it the Heavens below, in the underworld, orchestrated by the Wiggly Wickochettes.

The yellow ray swept upward
making way for the next descendant:
the orange ray.
All emotions could be felt on Earth.
The Creature awoke
and awakened feelings in our Pioneers.

CHAPTER SIX

The collective whole in the 49th Dimension renewing together
Opening gateways of cocreative possibilities forever
Smokeless radiant fire burning eternally within
Creative inspiration sparking Breath into a four directional wind

— **Orange**

azoom Boom-Zatten. A solar storm ignited from a single helical breath and echoed within the infinite time-space continuum. The Voice broke through the sound barrier shattering into Earth's atmosphere and spun the Pioneers into a muddled state, scattering them everywhere. It was the first time they felt emotionally confused. In journeys past, polarity and emotions did not exist, as all possible scenarios were weighed and measured on the cosmic scale that balanced spatial vibratory activities. Universal laws were fashioned on Earth to help Humans explore polarity-charged dramas. The Voice, impressed with how his plan was unfolding, pivoted around, smiled, and then looped into a time warp to secure a better vantage point.

From its planetary conception, Earth was groomed for a very special position in this galaxy. She was granted the privilege to care for the Sentient Emotion Generator (SEG). The SEG, an incredible galactic device, could sort and register kavillions of polarized bits and bytes into full operative experiences. Its supersonic function program and real time reactor module could spew out electromagnetic responses, calling lifeforms to react or to take action. The SEG's charge was fired up in two ways — either by Earth's electrically charged attributes, brought into play by Veteko, Illepio and Betern, or by Earth's warm magnetically charged attributes exuded by Yegerte, Orenga and Regeta. Gerpy chose the neutral role of providing leverage between two opposing forces and creating overall spectral equilibrium.

"Now that the cosmic curtain has risen and the SEG is functioning, one can view polarity in action, as infinite time on Earth emerges across the universal mirror." GrandPa enthusiastically projected.

"The Voice unleashed every emotion, action and event, and their reflected outcome, into play. The SEG served its purpose." GrandPa turned the dial and said

THE SENTIENT EMOTION GENERATOR

to the Children, "Take a glance at the Earth's future history books. You can see collective emotional events and personal dramas resulting from polarity fluctuations due to human decision-making processes and free will. No one knows exactly where the Voice hid the SEG. Perhaps it lies under the Wickochettes' control, deep within the underworld, along with the captured half of the rainbow that was hidden from Earth." GrandPa concluded as he switched back to the story.

"The SEG program emotionally animates lifeforms and also shapes Earthly landscapes and scenery. Just look at the effect it has already had on the Pioneers." added Greppy Graviton, as he observed their transformations and his own personal perception of Earthly matter.

"All scenes are sparked by thought and end in form alignment," GrandPa continued, "A single star point coordinate is marked in space, followed by another one, and so on. By connecting the star points, geometry shapes the framework of physicality and is animated by the infusion of color carried by our Pioneers." GrandPa concluded, as the laws of polarity were set into motion, the Children could roam within its depth and scope of possibilities.

The Voice recorded the Children's anticipation and then projected his attention onto Earth, where he reviewed the development of the mountains, forests and waterways that he was creating.

The universal mirror zoomed in on an unidentifiable dark force closing in on the Pioneers. The sheer force of the space disk burst through the atmosphere nearly smashing Earth into celestial debris. The Wickochettes slid their space disk through a stargate's sliver-sized opening and plunged down towards Earth in an attempt to terrorize the Pioneers. They sent hackling sonic waves and chilly vibrations to greet the Pioneers, longing to lure the photonic seven back into space where they could scuffle it out like galactic warriors. In response, the Pioneers firmly anchored their orbs to Earth to avoid being sucked into the Wickochettes' dark vibrations.

The Wickochettes' powerful forcefield entrapped Earth within its unyielding energy. Their space disk wavered furiously as they tapped into the ionosphere looking for additional power. Swerving around a huge mountain range and over massive bodies of water, the Wickochettes updated their territorial maps and prepared for certain conquest. They were unwavering and had set their minds on capturing the sapphire scepter. They had turned over every comet and asteroid in space, but to no avail. They needed the Pioneers' radar-tracking device to locate the scepter's coordinates. Once captured, and examined on the scalactic scale, the Pioneers would have no choice but to surrender.

The disturbance gathered cosmic forces. With a powerful heave, a twister-like funnel spliced apart the tenuous energy chains that imprisoned the Pioneers and prevented Earth from spinning freely. Earth gasped with relief as the Wickochettes slyly slithered off and backtracked through the stargate they had entered moments before. They would return at a more opportune moment, when they were least expected.

Swerchhhhh! The Voice changed into a colossal archetypal hand and dipped down through the ionosphere into the Earth's crust. The Earth's sedimentary layers trembled and crumbled at his touch. She began to quake. A huge mass of blackened clay was scooped up from deep within her body. The void in her belly immediately self-repaired as if nothing had scraped her brittle surface. The skies darkened, a lightning bolt flashed and thundered downward, striking a most unlikely target — the clay below.

Bombarded by electrical shocks, a Creature emerged and began to push its torso out of the muck. It spun around chaotically — shuddering, quivering and evolving through jolts of atomic spins and spindles. The electrical chaos flung the Children of the Multiverse across diverse dimensions and they multiplied in many worldly realms. Family chains of Protons, Neutrons, Electrons, and even Atoms were scattered across the galaxy. The Gravitons, Particles and Waves bilocated to a different storyline before the storm began, and Dudey Dust filled the skies with his presence, becoming a protective shield for the group.

THE VOICE CHANGED INTO A COLOSSAL ARCHETYPAL HAND AND DIPPED INTO THE EARTH'S CRUST

The Children collected their senses and returned to the spinning golden disk as if they had never left GrandPa's side. The precipitating Particle and the wandering Wave spoke, "The cosmos can try to break us down into little pieces and replicate us, but let us remind you that each piece is also a whole and will keep our ancestral image intact." The Children giggled as their own cosmic chains transcended to other galaxies, scattering in all directions, to colonize new realities.

Again and again slings of electrifying lightening bolts struck the Creature's emerging form. "Eyoowwweeeeeeeeee…" the Creature sounded an eerie scream from a fine opening on the front of its head. The lightning bolts were too intense for the Creature, as its curdling sounds ricocheted off space's outer periphery and stellar structures began to crumble from the intense vibrations. The Creature's Earthly composite began to simmer down and expand outward in the four directions. It had a semi-spherical shape with four appendages extending out from the center of its form. Both the upper and lower branches ended in compact clumps with five much smaller twigs. "The Creature is conscious!" Gerpy excitedly transmitted, as the Creature nearly stumbled over while getting its bearings. "It is not only massive, but clumsy," Regeta added, as the thing steadied itself, stood erect and gazed blankly into the skies. It became motionless as stillness finally filled the atmosphere.

The lightning bolts that coursed through the Creature had also rippled through the Pioneers as they deeply dug their tentacles into the cold clay-like composition at its base. Yegerte sensed that the Creature appeared to be erratic and unpredictable, yet stood apparently unaffected by their presence. The Creature's dry outer layer began to parch and flake off, as it shivered from the surges of energy beneath its surface.

The Pioneers picked up a distress signal coming from the Creature's body. The Creature was missing a detectable life source, but was not just a pile of muck. According to Veteko's radar, it appeared to have an electrically-charged conductive layer. "Although it was physically formed from Earth's crust, it definitely has cosmic appeal and a remarkable presence." said Betern in a collected manner.

"Were they able to identify the location of the Creature's life source?" Petky Proton questioned.

"Its life spark's secret location vanished with Subbie Consciousness. When she ricocheted off the looking glass and spiraled out of Siptrom Galaxy's infinite bandwidth, she hid Humankind's essence." GrandPa solemnly added, "But I do believe that the Wiggly Wickochettes were somehow involved in Subbie's disappearance."

The Children watched closely as the Pioneers began to express individual characteristics and finely tune their perceptions of Earthly reality. The Pioneers were metamorphosing through the SEG's influence. Their master program silently transformed them into an emotionally-charged photonic cluster with a far greater purpose.

"The evolving humanoid was preparing itself for life on Earth. If it wasn't for the heroic Pioneers, it could have remained a time-trapped marionette of muck." GrandPa recited from his mental notes, as he recalled this particular story had also played throughout other galaxies.

Illepio took the lead and declared, "We are invincible and have successfully orchestrated galaxies, star colonies, life on other planets and the gala of the galaxies. Other lifeforms from many dimensional planes have become self-sufficient due to our spectral assistance."

Gerpy was becoming slightly emotional. He had drifted off from the others and floated on a moonbeam to reflect upon Earth's consciousness. He felt overwhelmed that her surroundings lacked full-spectral vitality. Earth didn't yet have a color pallet. She was a feminine beauty awaiting the alluring shades of red, orange, yellow, green, blue, indigo and violet and every hue in between, that beautified nature in other galaxies.

A flash sparked from the core of each Pioneer. It was a message of gratitude from the Calinger Clouds, who wished them well. The group slowly released their thoughts to the winds and began to float along the solar currents. Their glistening bodies formed an exquisite star-shaped hologram of light. The Voice appeared and while gently lifting the prismatic array granted the Pioneers' encoded wish to create the Creature's inner processes.

The group suddenly sky-rocketed into the ionosphere and spiraled towards outer space. Calinger Clouds acted quickly by cushioning their trajectory. They bounced off her puffed-out chest and landed on top of the Creature's massive body. They left an assortment of rainbow splatterings — every color under the Sun — atop its form.

Subconsciously, within its own destiny program, the Creature knew of the Pioneers' Earthly mission. The group decided to reassess the transformation occurring in the Creature beneath them. The Creature jerked, sending out an electric shock of awareness, as Orenga and Illepio examined its response mechanisms with their micro-detector scope. Veteko's Calometer identified the star coordinates that may have influenced the Creature when they first landed upon her.

"This is definitely peculiar muck," Yegerte sputtered with muddied emotion, as Veteko received a flash reminder of feeling trapped on a terrain eons ago.

Silence cradled Earth's outer atmosphere. The Pioneers tweaked their antennas into position and stilled their senses in order to be more receptive to incoming cosmic data. Suddenly, cosmic radiation enveloped Earth's body creating an internal pressure. Physical development was a very difficult time for a planetary body.

"We are online and the reception is crystal clear," Veteko transmitted to her team. She felt familiar sensations as she located and identified the Creature's primordial spark. Its genesis originated in Siptrom Galaxy's 49th Dimension. The being's galactic blueprint was recorded in the Calometer for future reference.

"Secure your centers space mates; we are about to launch our internal investigation of the Creature," conducted Veteko as she primed her antenna and noted, "I've identified seven main vortices extending from the Creature's structure and aligning down its central column."

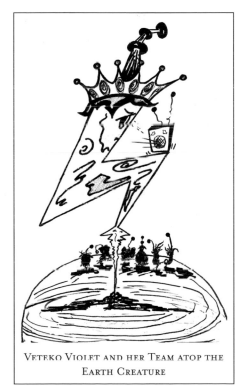

"These vortices are energy centers and connect here at this central gate." Illepio said reassuringly, after she had a chance to look into the opening with her inner vision. Her radar indicated that the central channel was designed to transport opposing

VETEKO VIOLET AND HER TEAM ATOP THE EARTH CREATURE

energy forces along the entire length of the Creature. Illepio was slightly perplexed and then realized that Salunken and Earth were directly linked to the Creature's core operating system."

The Creature picked up on Illepio's thoughts and made its overhead passageway accessible by tilting its head forward. Its right side was at an angle perpendicular to its left foot, as it clumsily shifted into place. Its concave mid-portion folded awkwardly downward. The Creature began to radiate an inner light, luring the Pioneers closer to its core. It raised its upper left limb, imitating a constellation, in an attempt to persuade the team to settle within its body.

"Its orbital position is a scaled reflection of Salunken's solar system in this dimension!" Betern enthusiastically shared, as she realized that everything existed in one eternal moment."

Illepio focused her visors, narrowing her microscopic view onto the Creature's skeletal structure. She saw that its tubular framework protected its inner world from potential outer invasion. "Ah, that's why it wasn't clear at first glance," Yegerte noted and continued, "The lightening bolts have quickened the Creature's rate of metamorphosis. It seems to be evolving right under our nuclei, as we transmit!"

Based upon his observations, Gerpy assumed the Creature had been hooked-up to the SEG and concluded that the sentient being generated and responded to emotional stimuli in this three-dimensional realm. Gerpy lifted his antenna and relayed his findings to the team. "For life to have sentient appeal, all feelings and perceptual tuners must register with the *Cosmic Code of Conductivity* and reside within that being's internal program center. The Voice's expansion plan is directed through breath and Earth forms are brought to life by the Sun. It appears that every breath fires internal communications that are subsequently echoed throughout their galaxy!"

GrandPa smoothed down his whithers, noting Gerpy's latest observation. "The Pioneers must have the magical ability to transform any dream into a worldly reality! My stardust can also construct inner realities just like the stellar structures I've built in space." Dudey cheerfully acknowledged the bigger picture. "As you can see Dudey, an Earthly reality is easy to shape once you have correctly positioned its star point coordinates." reassured GrandPa.

In honor of the red ray
the orange ray separated
bringing unity to the other frequency colors.
Discover the Pioneers' and Childrens' alliance
compounded together till this day.
Inward with outward color perceptions,
Humankind and Nature grateful forevermore.

CHAPTER
SEVEN

Gravitational forces aligning and merging cosmic essence
Uniting a chemical symbiotic system for sentient presence
Creating colorful firmaments of the Earth terrain
Colorizing nature with polarity in the Humankind domain

— Red

*T*he patter of Earth's heart calmed to a gentle beat preventing
her powerful core from erupting in waves of emotion. She felt
enormous inner power. She was aware that she could cast and sustain
life and that her child could support the universal mind. Salunken
beamed acknowledging Earth's new maturity and solarized the
atmosphere with every known frequency to influence the Earth
child's development.

The Pioneers synchronistically adjusted their vibratory cores to
harmonize with Earth's heartbeat. They balanced themselves on top
of the Creature by contracting their light bodies and inhaling their

respective colors to expand their mass. Then they cautiously examined and prodded at a crack on the surface that was bubbling and slightly oozing. The opening appeared to be spherical, deep and almost crater-like.

"Children, the cosmic clock has struck 11:11, which is your time to activate life on Earth." GrandPa said, "Although objective time has always stood still within the hologram of light, in your new Earthly continuum time appears to move forward." The Children listened intently as he continued, "Earth is now aligned with universal design, and sufficiently influenced by polarity to activate sentient life. Up until this point you have explored this story from two alternating realities separated by the universal mirror. Now reality has shifted."

Mischievously, the Children began oscillating above the spinning disk, preparing to teleport to Earth for permanent residency status. GrandPa remained silent as they vanished and reappeared inside of the Creature. The Creature jerked upon their impact. Instinctually, the Children formed the Creature's seven hollow chambers to align with its central force. GrandPa watched as they zipped busily about, when suddenly they stopped. They felt tentacles exploring the Creature's surface and something poking at their new-found home.

"Emissions are coming from the top of its head," Alte Atom echoed as the rest of the Children panicked and inadvertently set off a universal distress call. Screeeeech! The piercing sounds of cosmic sirens echoed throughout space reverberating within the Creature's inner centers. The GGG was fully notified. The group's prodding caused the Creature's wheel-like craters to spin into a furious state of activation; they creaked and sprang into full rotation, incrementally expanding as their speed increased.

"We've created a big ruckus for this pile of muck." Betern transmitted to the GGG, "... We are still acting in strict accordance with the galactic *Protocol of Non-Interference* ... A false red alert was activated." The sirens stopped screeching as Regeta notified the others, "It's definitely awake, the crater at the Creature's peak is moving faster and faster!"

Illepio's inspected the opening and identified faint eerie cries echoing along the Creature's inner channel. "Oh, it's just another colony of space travelers exploring the structure from the inside out," she told her team.

"Declare yourselves! State your galaxy, constellation and purpose for occupation in our timeline!" insisted Veteko to the voices within. But the Children remained precisely where the Voice had positioned them. When they realized that they were talking to the Pioneers from GrandPa's story, they began to playfully taunt them.

"Drop in and join us down here," the childlike sounds innocently coaxed. "These voices seem to have ulterior motives." Veteko conveyed to Illepio. Another wave of emotion washed over her as she tuned into the Children's voices. Illepio's consciousness was becoming emotionally receptive for the first time in her existence. Feeling awkward Illepio adjusted her visors, assessed the situation and attuned her sensitivity levels accordingly.

Steadily, the vortex rotated expanding in diameter as its speed increased with momentum. Being nourished by the ionosphere's radiation, the vortex drew in vast quantities of energy, and the more it consumed, the more it cravingly hungered for more. As the group focused and calculated the perimeter, they positioned their tentacles and then firmly anchored them to the Creature's head. The Creature's quantum force became stronger as its internal electrical system was triggered, thirsting for a deeper union with the Pioneers.

"This Creature is extremely demanding." blurted Orenga, as he shifted from his sunny self into feelings of annoyance. Gerpy immediately anchored Orenga and then reverted back to his own balanced vibratory state.

Violet! Indigo! Blue! Green! Yellow! Orange! Red!

Suddenly, the vortex's suctioning became too great a pressure for the Pioneers. In a single breath, they sounded off their respective frequencies as they were drawn deeply into the spiraling funnel. Colorful flashes lit the passageway. The intensity of the Creature's internal pressure caused them to release their grip and they tumbled downward, with the exception of Veteko who got lodged in the Creature's uppermost opening.

> *"Here we go down the spiraling hole,*
> *Emotions and feelings we've come to know.*
> *Understanding that what we reap is what we sow.*
> *Advise of stargate exit from this energy flow."*

Veteko quickly switched on her Calometer. Its cosmically clear reception registered a ticker of the following alert:

"... DESTINATION IMPRINTED: COSMIC CLEARANCE APPROVED FOR HUMAN EXPLORATION."

"What? Nonsensical. Recalibrate. Continue transmitting." Veteko, wildly confused, shook her antenna. Emotional confusion. "Coordinates may have been altered or a malevolent force may have sent scrambled codes to our program." she replied to the Galactic Council. Perhaps the Wiggly Wickochettes had encrypted a decoy outline within the expansion plan. The Pioneers had been notified that Earth's gravity field held positively good vibrations, so why had an opposing tension amplified this timeline?

Fleeting thoughts of the Wickochettes rode across Veteko's bandwidth. Had they secretly installed a glitch in the SEG program? She dismissed the idea of a wickedly-warped plot, remembering that random acts of free will consciousness were an aspect of the Voice's bigger plan, which included choices between good and evil vibrations. Veteko tried to contact her team, but surges of evil sensations began to oscillate and prowl in her midst, creating intense emotional pressure. She became uncontrollably erratic and slam-dunked her Calometer. It twisted and flung out through the vortex's opening, into outer galactic space, never to be found. She took a deep breath to calm her rattled senses into respectable order.

The photonic seven continued to plummet down the inner walls of the Creature sinking deeper and deeper into form. They were separated according to wavelength and individually traveled down the energy channel to predestined locations. Although still independently mindful, the Pioneers preferred to collaborate while on the Earthly plane and found their predicament most unusual.

Boom.

Red! Orange! Yellow! Green! Blue! Indigo! Violet!

Luminous explosions reverberated throughout the Creature's inner cage-like structure and rattled Gerpy's chamber. Illepio took her position and examined the seven vortices that were an extension of their chambers. "These vortices are the gateways into the Creature's mind." she communicated to her comrades.

The Pioneers fashioned their chambers within the seven energy centers. The magnetic photons were drawn further down the Creature's column than the electric ones. Aligned by wavelength, they were placed directly underneath each other. Regeta landed at the tip of the

Creature's spinal column. "Believe it, or not, it's a long way down!" Regeta breathlessly echoed upward, "This is a force that cannot be diffused." Regeta nearly lost his vital energy source as he fell into his allotted place.

They settled into their energy centers and welcomed a golden ray who was sent to them by the Galactic Council carrying the following message: "You are transitioning and morphing into forms that will be of service to the Creature. Your magical presence has triggered the full integration of SEG sequence patterns into the Creature's operating program." Greppy Graviton assisted the Creature by playfully grounding the Pioneer's light. The Children continued to taunt and tease the Pioneers triggering more deeply held emotions.

Veteko investigated a maze of narrow interconnected channels linked to each center, "Imperative energy conduits to animate physical life!" she notified the others. Illepio diligently tracked her team's coordinates. "A crystalline prism in my periphery has separated us." she transmitted, as she settled into the central part of the Creature's head. Detecting a colorless rotating vortex behind her, she cautiously lengthened her receptors to investigate and then retracted them. Illepio then honed her radar in on Veteko. "Veteko, was your landing pad steady?" catching a faint glimpse of violet sparks and spirals overhead. "Feeling violetly invigorated!" Veteko regally echoed, however, she did feel slightly isolated at the Creature's apex.

Squeezing her body into a bolt of light enabled Veteko to narrowly observe their point of entry as she excitedly squirted violet sparks everywhere. She elongated her antenna stretching out its sensory nodule to explore the translucent energy stream overflowing from the vortex, but its force seized her and absorbed her radiance. The vortex transformed into a cosmic array of violet, lavender and lilac energies, overflowing with effervescent purple froth along its rim. Composing herself, Veteko confidently joined forces with the Children who now resided near the apex of the Creature's physical body.

Illepio zoomed her attention upward to observe this magical act. Enchanted, she followed Veteko who had signaled for her to proceed. Illepio irradiated an indigo beam into the adjacent spinning vortex. Frequencies of indigo blue, sapphire, and azure laced with golden twirls, filled her vision. The vibrations excited the wheel, which increased its momentum and lit up the Creature's head. Satisfied with her photonic artistry, Illepio merged with the Children who resided below Veteko's energy center.

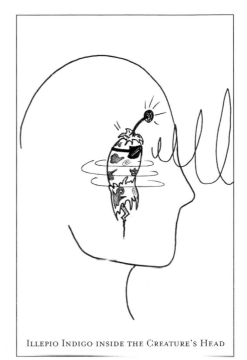

ILLEPIO INDIGO INSIDE THE CREATURE'S HEAD

Descending along the column, Betern stumbled into her center attempting to recalibrate back into her photonic state. Noticing an alluring vortex in front of her nucleus, overwhelming sensations floated throughout her inner space. She poured out, "I need to speak and be heard!" and then erratically flung herself into the energy wheel. "Yippeeeeeeeee!" Betern bubbled as she was playfully tossed out from its centripetal force. The vortex tapped into Betern's quintessence and transmuted into a shimmering spiral that flowed with frequencies of sky blue, cobalt and turquoise overtones. Betern then floated over to greet her childlike friends below the Creature's head.

Gerpy happily radiated his essence into his vortex which swirled with exquisite shades of emerald green, chartreuse and jade. Gerpy joined the Children residing in the Creature's upper torso. Gerpy's responsibility was to balance all vibrational activity. He sensed agitated emissions coming from Yegerte below. "Explore this magical experience — it will offer clarity and dissolve your uneasiness!" Gerpy encouraged.

Yegerte was magnetically drawn into his vortex and released yellow, gold and caramel vibrations igniting the wheel into activation. Yegerte elatedly twirled in his energy reservoir and then united with the Children in the Creature's adjoining mid-torso. Yegerte's new job was to monitor the Creature's stress level as it could affect all of the other centers.

Orenga blasted an orange beam onto a central point of his vortex and it suddenly swirled with orange, peach and tangerine streamers that funneled towards the Creature's lower torso, a most creative energy center. The Children drew in his radiance, thrilled to have Orenga as their magical ally!

Regeta had been watching the activity above and sensing it was his turn, aimed fiery radiations directly into his vortex emblazing it with red, scarlet, ruby and crimson swirls. Regeta joined the Children located in the energy center at the tip of the spinal column, and sent his grounding support to the six higher centers. He linked himself to Earth's pristine core, tapping into her source, and channeled it into the Creature. Veteko then instinctively drew universal energy down through her center and into the other six. All was well: the Pioneers were finally in place.

ುುುುು

Stilling his vacuum-pressured mind, the Voice's radar honed onto a faint familiar vibration. Could it possibly be? Indeed! The Voice excitedly funneled his energy to the four directions. Vatock Brimmel-Frock. Subbie Consciousness teasingly nudged his forcefield and

SUBBIE CONSCIOUSNESS TEASINGLY NUDGED THE VOICE'S FORCEFIELD

emerged with a sonic blast, and then lovingly encircled the Voice in a tempting embrace.

"The Voice is not the only Force to make grand appearances." GrandPa chuckled to himself, as he watched the galactic romance. "It has been eons-of-ions since her looking glass escapade, and she has returned just in time."

She was a most elegant galactic being. Boasting cosmic wisdom, she fully supported the Voice's knowledge and agenda. The Voice could hardly contain himself. To be back in close radiation with his dream-force coiled him into a blazing electrical state. Subbie calmed the Voice and gently rested on his consciousness. Their scalarly-stretched separation had been almost too much to withstand.

Subbie wavered in delight and asserted her feminine influence over Earth. She then infused the Pioneers and Children with the missing element of the expansion plan: Humankind would learn of their origin and be bestowed with universal powers. Subbie would respect Humanity's choices and only communicate with Humans via the subconscious mind.

The Calinger Clouds darkened and rolled quickly by. The ionosphere quaked with trepidation as the Voice emitted a rumble that rippled across Earth's surface. The Creature shivered and shook from the surge. The Voice appeared before the Creature, "Is the seven-tiered energy system now online, Veteko?" "All internal structures and grids are calibrated and aligned to the expansion plan's specifications." she transmitted with authority. Veteko activated the switch of sentient-ability.

Trumpen Krebem-Zolp. The Creature was now cosmically online and connected to light intelligence. The electrical circuitry jump-started the Creature into activation. The Children began to build up the Creature's anatomical systems and improve its motor functions. The Creature awkwardly twitched her head and wrenched her neck. Still shuddering from the electrical shock of awakening, she gasped her first breath, and shivered in the cool air. The Voice immediately enveloped her with his warming breath and the Calinger Clouds retracted to let Salunken's sunshine in.

Subbie linked her subtle energies to the Creature's body and instructed the SEG generator to integrate her caring wisdom with the Creature's free will. The Voice calmed his solar radiation and stilled his presence. His breath transferred an inner knowingness that glistened in her eyes. She touched her face and peeled back crumbling muck to reveal a most distinguishing Human trait — conscious self-awareness, along with her new silky smooth complexion!

Glistening in the Salunkian sunlight, her golden tresses inconspicuously concealed the entranceway to the Pioneers' new home. Shockwaves softly rippled along her figure lighting up her internal channels and smoothing her body into a sleek elegant form. She gently composed herself and desired a flowing body drapery. Beautiful swirling lights magically appeared courtesy of the Pioneers and wove themselves into a finely textured gown. Satisfied, she was now fully cloaked in fashionable rainbow attire and was a lady of great light.

"The Creature has crystallized into a graceful Human lady!" GrandPa said approvingly.

Forcing the air from her lungs, she cleared her throat preparing to utter her first words. The Calinger Clouds waved merrily above as the Lady fluttered her eyelids in acknowledgement. "I can speak," the Lady bashfully croaked in a deep pitch, embarrassed by her vocal tone.

Finally free from the bondage of petrified muck, and feeling lighter and lighter, she arched her back, rolled her shoulders, and took long stretches backward, forward, and from side to side. Her body elongated and magically curved in at Yegerte's and out at Orenga's energy centers. She raised her hands overhead and twirled around and around, physically charged by Regeta Red.

Betern Blue coaxed the Lady's voice to soften into several octaves of sweet tones. She cleared her throat again and gracefully spoke with clarity and self-assurance. "I have a vague recollection of speaking," she pondered, as her mind flashed back to a vision through a looking glass, but she couldn't exactly remember where or when that was. Veteko and Illepio encouraged her thought processes and kept her communicative network operating in perfect harmony.

Suddenly, Veteko detected an ominous sulphuric scent. The Wiggly Wickochettes were in close proximity! Gerpy took immediate charge and shut the Lady's seven stargate openings with his loving kindness as the wiggly wicked ones sent nasty vibrations to the Lady's energy field, attempting to torment her consciousness with their wily words.

THE WIGGLY WICKOCHETTES WERE IN CLOSE PROXIMITY TO THE LADY

"Well my dear, ... hmmmm .... think you're quite the charming one, do you? ... You've morphed from a cosmic spark of sheer nothingness to the epitome of Human kindness: a wingless, beakless, flaking thing! ... Ekkem!! ... eternally hiding the Pioneers in your body is not a sensible choice. You can choose good or evil in this Earthly matter ... surrender those despicable Pioneers and their juvenile accomplices ... Teleport them to us without delay or we will vaporize you and pulverize your pretty home into putrefied pulp! Or, if you are a clever girl, you can join us on our odyssey exploring the black underworldly realms. Light is nice but darkness is out of this world!"

And with those sinister words, the Wickochettes sensed a benevolent vibrational force rapidly approaching and spat out an inky cloud of gaseous black gunk. They coldly concluded, "We'll be back, my dear, for the Pioneers' sapphire scepter, as we also have free will." Suddenly, the Wickochettes' communications were static; their space disk went offline and sputtered away on a beam of black light.

The Lady's heartbeat returned to beat in tune with the Earth's. She gazed at a calming rainbow drawn across the skies and dismissed the nastiness of her wiggly visitors. Through a crack in her inner perception, the Pioneers inquisitively peered out, inspired by her newly formed wishes. The Lady was in the mood to decorate her Earthly abode with colorful scenery, flora and fauna.

Projecting colored beams, the Pioneers magically transformed Earth into a breathtaking haven enriched with radiant living color. Orenga Orange began by tapping into his creative reservoir and, fueled by Regeta Red, they ignited the other Pioneers who fully calibrated their color beams and painted Earth's landscape.

The Lady gently lay on a bed of flowers and fell into a deep slumber as the Pioneers continued coloring in Earth's beautiful environment.

The Lady's dreams formed many new kingdoms: air, water, mineral, plant and animal. She vividly illuminated a wilderness of spectacular forests, flowering fields and countless species of trees with blossoms. Color frequencies bounced off Earth striking the delectable fruit above and then rebounded downward and enriched the vegetables below. The grass breathed in Gerpy Green's essence and covered the rolling hillsides. The barren terrain filled with shrubbery that stretched beside a lush oasis and flowing blue waterways. All kingdoms now overflowed with dazzling color. All Earthly beauty was born from the Lady's endless imagination.

The Lady awoke and groggily opened her eyes. She sat up speechlessly staring across the horizon knowing this was, but wasn't, a dream and that she could perpetually create new realities with the help of her inner friends. She possessed the visionary ability to creatively guide all the kingdoms of Earth.

"Humankind is now self-sufficient, and Earth has fulfilled her role to nurture living frequencies sparked from the cosmic realms." the Voice proclaimed. Earth momentarily stood still, as influential stars shuffled into new arrangements to impart their benevolent frequencies upon Humankind, and then she decided to spin in the opposite direction. "Just as we planned, my moonbeam of thought!" the Voice said to Subbie as they merged into a unified Force. "Earth has earned the authentic power to govern herself and protect the sapphire scepter in her ionosphere."

Crackle Zippen-Poof. The unified Force funneled upward, splicing through the continuum and stretching its energy beyond the fringes of outer galactic space, primed for its next mission: to awaken Human lifeforms on the next planetary body of Salunken's solar system.

ജ്ഞംജ്ഞംജ്ഞ

GrandPa swung around on his cushion, relishing the expansion plan's victory on Earth. Earth's ionosphere safely held the wisdom and knowledge of the sapphire scepter and was embedded with the Voice and Subbie Consciousness' combined essence forevermore. GrandPa quietly turned off the projector and plotted the next journey for the unified Force on his stellar agenda. He took a deep breath and exhaled with a boom, moving the dial on the cosmic clock past 11:11.

EPILOGUE

The end never existed,
nor did its beginning take place.
The Dream within a dream.
Its Breath. Its Boom.
This colorful Mindful Space.

The odyssey of the cosmic masquerade,
A mystical and magical evolutionary parade.
You are the Dream of creation
and every aspect in between.
Be the characters personified in each animated scene.

You are All.

The Children.
GrandPa GammaRay.
The Pioneers.
The Wiggly Wickochettes.
Salunken the Sun.
The Stars.
The Earth.
The Sapphire Scepter.
Subbie Consciousness.

The Voice within and the Voice afar.

Animate creation, reclaim your fate,
Design an outline, and engrave on life's slate.
Unlimited opportunities, possibilities to discover,
Eternity is your Thought expanding forever.

Once within a time-space continuum, eons before perception,
When time stood still, rose the birth of cosmic conception.
Each moment free-will choice is birthed anew,
Light — the universal worldly realms of you.